30 SOLDERI

CW00543574

30 SOLDERLESS BREADBOARD PROJECTS
BOOK 1

by
R. A. Penfold

BERNARD BABANI (publishing) LTD
THE GRAMPIANS
SHEPHERDS BUSH ROAD
LONDON W6 7NF
ENGLAND

PLEASE NOTE

© 1982 BERNARD BABANI (publishing) LTD

First Published — October 1982
Reprinted — October 1988

British Library Cataloguing in Publication Data
Penfold, R. A.
   30 solderless breadboard projects — book 1 (BP107)
   1. Electronic circuits
   I. Title
   621.3815'3   TK9965

ISBN 0 85934 082 1

Printed and bound in Great Britain by Cox & Wyman Ltd, Reading

PREFACE

Although the sophistication and complexity of electronic equipment seems to continually increase, it is still possible to produce simple and useful electronic devices that even a complete beginner can tackle with confidence. The purpose of this book is simply to provide a number of designs of this type. A few of the designs are intended mainly to demonstrate the operation of a particular type of component or circuit, but most have a practical application or applications.

No prior knowledge of electronic components and constructional techniques is necessary in order to build the thirty designs featured here, and construction is made easier by the use of a Verobloc breadboard as the constructional basis of all the projects. Component layout and wiring diagrams are provided for each project, and as the components are simply plugged into the Verobloc, and leads to off-board components (such as controls) can be fitted with crocodile clips which connect to these components without the need for any soldering, it is a simple matter to assemble each project. It is also an easy matter to dismantle a project and reuse the components when building a subsequent project. The circuits have been designed so that wherever possible components are common to several of the designs, and with only a modest number of components that are reasonably inexpensive it is possible to build (in turn) every project featured in this book! The only tools required are a pair of wire cutters and strippers, a pair of pliers, and a small screwdriver.

It is not essential to use a Verobloc breadboard as the basis of the projects, and it should be possible to use other solderless breadboards such as manufactured by Global Specialties Corporation (GSC) or Boss Industrial Mouldings Ltd, etc. However, as the layout diagrams provided in this book are specifically for the Verobloc breadboard it would probably be advisable for complete beginners to use one of these, although most other breadboards use a similar arrangement and readers with some previous experience of electronics could probably use an alternative breadboard with little or no difficulty. Please note that alternative breadboards may have different letter and number markings to those shown in this book for Verobloc.

Solderless breadboards are not usually used as the basis for *permanent* projects, but once the reader has gained some practical experience by breadboarding some of the projects, he or she should have little difficulty in building the projects on stripboard or using some other conventional constructional method.

The components employed in the designs in this book are virtually all quite common types that are much used in home-constructor designs, and any "left-overs" should prove useful as a stock of components for future use. Similarly, the bread-board should be useful for experimenting with simple designs other than those featured in this book, and is likely to receive many years of heavy use.

R. A. Penfold

CONTENTS

CHAPTER 1

USING A BREADBOARD

The term "breadboard" is one that is likely to be a little confusing to beginners, but it simply means a board on which electronic circuits can be built and tested. Modern breadboards are almost invariably of the solderless type, where components are simply plugged in and unplugged as desired. Apart from the obvious advantage of enabling circuit changes to be rapidly made when experimenting, it also enables components to be reused almost indefinitely. Components will in fact eventually wear out because the leadout wires will need to be reformed slightly to fit into new layouts, and the leadout wires eventually suffer from metal fatigue and break off (usually close to the body of the component so that it becomes useless). This can be overcome though by only using components for breadboarding for a limited period of time, and then using them in finished projects and getting a new stock of breadboarding components.

Although the term "breadboard" may seem inexplicable, it is probably derived from the early days of electronics when valved circuits were normally prototyped on a large wooden board (like a breadboard) into which nails were hammered. Components were then connected to the nails, and additional wires were used to connect the components in the desired fashion. Some finished equipment actually used this method of construction. A variation on this type of board was to use screw terminals so that no soldering was necessary; the original solderless breadboards, in fact!

Modern breadboards are much simpler and easier to use, and apart from being useful to experienced electronic engineers working on prototype designs, they also have attractions for beginners. One is simply that they are very easy to use, and anyone can plug in and remove components from a solderless breadboard; no previous experience of electronics construction being necessary. When the inevitable mistakes in the

1

component layout do occur, it is an easy matter to check through the layout and remedy the errors since no awkward desoldering is necessary. It is also easy to quickly build and experiment with a number of projects at low cost with everything involved being reusable, including the breadboard.

The breadboard used by the author when constructing the projects featured in this book was a Verobloc, and the component layouts provided are for this particular breadboard. The Verobloc uses the arrangement shown in Figure 1.

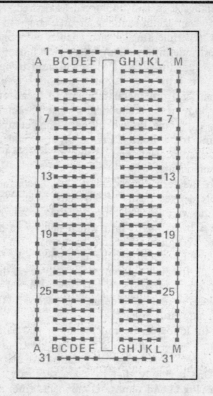

Fig. 1 The general arrangement of the Verobloc

Numbers are used to identify the horizontal rows of holes and letters are employed to identify the vertical rows of holes. In order to make it easier to copy component layouts the identification letters and some of the numbers are marked on the layout diagrams and on the Verobloc itself.

In Figure 1 lines are used between holes to show how they are internally interconnected and, for example, all the holes in row "A" are connected together. The rows of holes around the periphery of the board are mainly used to carry the two supply lines. The spacing of the holes is such that most integrated circuits can be plugged straight into the board without the need for any special adaptors, and this is certainly the case with the two integrated circuits used in the designs described in this publication. Each hole in the board is fitted with a spring terminal which will readily accept any component leadout wire or pin.

Controls and some other components do not plug straight into the board, but are mounted off-board on a mounting bracket of some kind, and connected to the board via single core insulated leads. Multistrand wire is normally used for interconnecting wires of this type, but multistrand wire can be difficult to connect to a solderless breadboard as the strands tend to splay as the wire is pushed into the board. If you have soldering equipment this can be overcome by tinning the ends of multistrand leads with solder, but it is otherwise better to use single strand wire. Any PVC-covered type that is not unusually thick or thin should be suitable (i.e. about 22 SWG).

A panel on which the controls can be mounted, and which will slot into the Verobloc can be obtained, but there is a slight problem in using this with some of the designs featured in this book because some of the control components are quite large and would obstruct the board. One way around this is to use two Veroblocs (they can be plugged together either side-by-side or end-to-end), one simply being used to space the controls away from the board that is used to carry the other components. Although the second Verobloc is not needed for the designs described in this book, it will almost certainly be put to use as you progress to more complex projects. An alternative method is to mount the Verobloc on a plywood or hardboard base fitted with an aluminium front panel on which the controls are mounted. The battery (all the designs use a PP6 9-volt type) can also be mounted on the baseboard using a simple mounting bracket fabricated from aluminium. Figure 2 gives details of a suitable general arrangement for the unit, but obviously any sensible layout can be employed. The potentio-

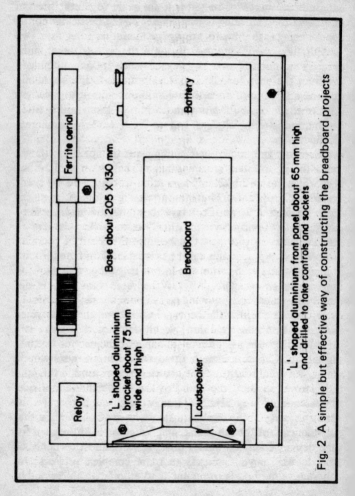

Fig. 2 A simple but effective way of constructing the breadboard projects

Ferrite aerial

Battery

Base about 205 X 130 mm

'L' shaped aluminium front panel about 65 mm high and drilled to take controls and sockets

Breadboard

Relay

'L' shaped aluminium bracket about 75 mm wide and high

Loudspeaker

meters and variable capacitor used in the circuits in this book need standard 10 mm diameter mounting holes. If the push-button switch used is of the usual inexpensive miniature type it will require a 7 mm diameter mounting hole. Most miniature toggle switches require a 6.4 mm (¼ in) diameter mounting hole, but some types require a smaller mounting hole of 5.2 mm (0.2 in) in diameter. It is advisable to check this by measuring the mounting-bush diameter of the particular component being used prior to drilling the mounting hole.

Although the Verobloc breadboard is solderless, the controls are not and have tags or pins which are only intended to take wires via soldered joints. Ideally single-strand insulated leads about 150 mm or so long should be soldered to the tags or pins of the controls, and about 5 mm of insulation should be removed from the free end of each lead to facilitate connection to the Verobloc breadboard. Fortunately there is an alternative method of connecting leads to the controls and this is simply to use crocodile clips. They have two small jaws which are pushed closed by a built-in spring, and the jaws are simply clipped over the appropriate tag or pin. With most crocodile clips it is not necessary to solder the leads to the clip, and there is either a screw which can be used to clamp the lead in place, or a couple of metal lugs which can be pressed down onto the lead using a pair of pliers and thus firmly fix it in place. In this application the best type of crocodile clip to use is probably one of the very small types having a PVC cover. These will clip onto the tags of potentiometers without overcrowding, and the PVC covers insulate the clips from one another so that accidental short circuits are avoided.

A few of the circuits use a telephone pick-up coil or a crystal earpiece, and these are both fitted with 3.5 mm jack plugs. One way of making the connections to these is to fit a 3.5 mm jack socket on the front panel of the breadboard unit, and then connect this to the board using crocodile clip leads in the same way that connections are made to the controls. Of course, the pick-up coil or earphone plug is plugged into the jack socket. An alternative method is simply to use a couple of crocodile clip leads to make the connections directly to the plug.

The connections to the battery are made via a battery clip of the appropriate type, and a PP6-size battery uses the same type of connector as the popular PP3 battery (and this type of connector is normally sold as a PP3 type even though it is actually used for other types of battery). The leads attached to the battery connector are almost certain to be of the multi-strand type, and as mentioned earlier, will not easily plug into a solderless breadboard. If it is not possible to tin the leads with solder so that the strands of wire are held together, simply twisting the strands of wire tightly together might be satisfactory. Another possibility is to fit the two leads with crocodile clips which can be clipped to a couple of pieces of single-strand wire (one clip to each piece of wire), and these two wires are then plugged into the breadboard.

Some of the projects use a loudspeaker, and this could be mounted on an aluminium panel fitted on the left-hand side of the breadboard assembly. Unfortunately most loudspeakers of the correct type do not have any built-in means of panel mounting, and it will either be necessary to glue the speaker in place, or some simple method of clamping it in place must be devised. If it is glued in place, use a good-quality adhesive such as a clear type or an epoxy one, otherwise in use it is likely that the speaker will simply come unstuck. Be careful to apply the adhesive only to the front outer rim of the speaker, and not onto the diaphragm (which could severely reduce the quality of the speaker). If this method of mounting is used it should be borne in mind that it will be difficult to remove the speaker for use elsewhere without at least slightly damaging it, although if it is carefully cut free it will almost certainly be found to be perfectly usable.

For experimental purposes it is not essential to have the speaker properly mounted at all, and it can simply be laid face downwards to one side of the breadboard assembly, preferably on a magazine or a few sheets of cardboard. This should provide an output of reasonable quality, although a small loudspeaker gives no significant bass response even if placed in a proper enclosure. Of course, the speaker can be fitted into a small cabinet if desired, and this will give optimum quality and volume.

The two connections to the loudspeaker can be made via a couple of crocodile clip leads, as for the other off-board components.

Components

The main problem for someone starting electronics as a hobby is simply that of identifying the various components used in projects. Before proceeding to the projects a brief description of the components used in them will be given so that even a complete beginner should have no difficulty in sorting out which component is which, and connecting each component into circuit correctly.

Resistors

These are small cylindrical components having a leadout protruding from each end. The value is not marked in numbers and letters, but is indicated by four coloured bands around the body of the component. The value is in units called "ohms", and resistors often have values of many thousands of ohms, or even a few million ohms. In order to avoid constantly using very large numbers it is common for resistance to be specified in kilohms (k) and megohms (M). These are equal to a thousand ohms and a million ohms respectively. Thus a resistor having a value of 33,000 ohms would normally be said to have a value of 33 k, and a resistor having a value of 2,700,000 ohms would normally have its value given as 2.7 M. It is common these days for the units symbol to be used to indicate the decimal point as well. This sometimes further shortens a value in its written form, and there is no danger of a decimal point being overlooked due to poor quality printing or something of this nature. In our two examples given above the value of 33 k would not be altered since the "k" already indicates the position of the decimal point, but 2.7 M would be altered to 2M7.

The resistor colour code is very straightforward, with the first two bands giving the first two digits of the value, the third band giving a multiplier (i.e. the first two digits are multiplied by this third figure in order to give the value of the component in ohms), and the fourth band showing the tolerance of the component. The resistor colour code is detailed below.

Colour	1st/2nd Band	3rd Band	4th Band
Gold	not used	0.1	5%
Black	0	0	not used
Brown	1	10	1%
Red	2	100	2%
Orange	3	1,000	not used
Yellow	4	10,000	not used
Green	5	100,000	not used
Blue	6	1,000,000	not used
Violet	7	not used	not used
Grey	8	not used	not used
White	9	not used	not used
Silver	not used	0.01	10%
No Band	not used	not used	20%

Thus, in the example shown in Figure 3 the first two digits of the value are 4 (yellow) and 7 (violet), giving 47 which must be multiplied by 100 (red), giving a value of 4,700 ohms. This would normally be written at 4.7 k or 4k7. The fourth band is gold which indicates that the value of the component is within

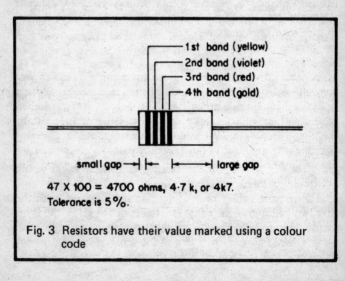

1st band (yellow)
2nd band (violet)
3rd band (red)
4th band (gold)

small gap →| |← |←   →| large gap

47 X 100 = 4700 ohms, 4·7 k, or 4k7.
Tolerance is 5%.

Fig. 3 Resistors have their value marked using a colour code

5% of its marked value. Note that it is perfectly all right to use a component having a closer tolerance than is specified in a components list (a 2% type can be used in place of a 5% type for example), but a component having a higher tolerance than that specified (such as a 10% type instead of a 5% type) is not acceptable.

Resistors also have a power rating, and this is not usually marked on the component (except in the case of high power types where the value and wattage may both be written on the component, no colour codes being used). For the circuits in this book ordinary miniature 1/8, 1/4, or 1/3 watt resistors are satisfactory since the power levels involved are very low. Higher power resistors are not really suitable, and this is due to their physical rather than electrical characteristics. Higher wattage resistors are physically quite large and would be difficult to fit into the available space, and some have very thick leadout wires which will not fit easily into solderless breadboards.

Incidentally, in order to aid the selection of a resistor of the correct value, all components lists in this book have the colour code for each resistor alongside the value. Thus, even if you do not understand the resistor colour-coding system you should still be able to pick out the appropriate resistors with the aid of the components lists.

Capacitors
Most capacitors used to look much the same as resistors but were normally a little larger and had the value written on their body rather than marked using a colour code. Modern capacitors are still generally somewhat larger than resistors, but they often have both leadout wires coming from the same end of the component as this makes them more convenient for use with printed circuit boards. Also, they often have rectangular rather than tubular bodies.

The projects featured in this book use several types of capacitor, including electrolytic types. These are available as axial (with the leadout wires coming from opposite ends of the component) and printed circuit types. Axial electrolytics were used when developing the projects, and the layout drawings

9

show the electrolytics as axial components, but printed circuit mounting types can be fitted into the layouts with no difficulty.

An important point to bear in mind with electrolytic capacitors is that they are polarised, and must be connected to the circuit the right way round (resistors, and most other types of capacitor can be connected either way round). In the component layouts given in this book the leadout wires are identified by "+" and "−" signs, and the leadout wires of the actual components are identified "+" and "−" signs on the bodies of the components. Additionally, axial types usually have an indentation around one end of the component's body, and this indicates the end of the component from which the positive (+) leadout wire emerges.

One of the capacitors used in a few projects is a tantalum bead type, and like an electrolytic capacitor this is a polarised component. Tantalum capacitors are normally small, bead-shaped components (which are sometimes called tantalum bead capacitors) which have both leadout wires coming from the same end of the body. The positive leadout wire should be identified by the appropriate sign marked on the body of the component. Be careful to connect the tantalum capacitor the right way round as capacitors of this type are easily damaged by a voltage of the wrong polarity.

Another type of capacitor used in the projects is a ceramic plate or disc ceramic type. Either type is suitable, and the only physical difference between the two is that the plate type is rectangular while the disc type is obviously circular. Capacitors of this type sometimes have the value written on the body of the component in a straightforward manner, but it is not unusual for the value to be marked using less than obvious figures. For example, the value might be given as 332, to indicate a value of 3.3 nF. The first two numbers give the first two digits of the value, and the third number indicates the number of zeros to be added to give the value in picofarads. Thus 332 indicates a value of 3,300 pF, and as 1,000 pF equals one nanofarad (1 nF), 3,300 pF equals 3.3 nF. Incidentally, larger capacitance values are usually given in microfarads (μF); 1 μF being equal to 1,000 nF or 1,000,000 pF.

10

The other fixed-value capacitors used in the projects are of the polyester variety, and the Mullard C280 type (or any similar type) will fit into the component layouts most readily. These are rectangular, printed-circuit-mounting capacitors, and are unusual in that the value is marked using a colour code. There are five coloured bands around the component, as shown in Figure 4, and the first three give the value of the component in the same way as the resistor colour code. However, the value is in picofarads rather than ohms. The last two bands show the tolerance and maximum working voltage of the component respectively. For the values used in the projects described in this book the last two bands will probably be black (20% tolerance) and red (250 volts DC maximum), but other colours are sometimes encountered, such as white (10%) and yellow (400 volts DC maximum). This is of no consequence, and any C280 polyester capacitors are suitable for use in these projects.

Where polyester components are specified in a components list, the appropriate colour code is given to aid the selection of the correct component.

The radio circuits use a variable capacitor, and this is in fact the tuning control. The specified type is a solid dielectric

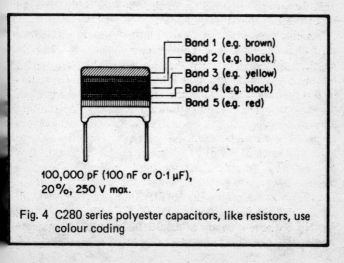

Band 1 (e.g. brown)
Band 2 (e.g. black)
Band 3 (e.g. yellow)
Band 4 (e.g. black)
Band 5 (e.g. red)

100,000 pF (100 nF or 0·1 µF),
20%, 250 V max.

Fig. 4 C280 series polyester capacitors, like resistors, use colour coding

component having a maximum capacitance of 300 pF, but any variable capacitor having a maximum value of about 200 pF to 300 pF is suitable from the electrical point of view. However, the specified "Dilecon" component manufactured by Jackson Brothers Ltd (and available from a number of the larger component retailers) has a standard 10 mm mounting bush and 6.4 mm (¼ in) spindle. Beware of cheaper types having mounting arrangements and (or) non-standard spindle sizes which would make them difficult to use.

Semiconductors

Several types of semicondutors are used in the projects, and we will start with the two transistors. Transistors have three leadout wires which are called the base, emitter, and collector. It is essential that these are connected correctly, as there is no chance of a project working if they are not. Fortunately modern transistors are not easily damaged, and incorrect connection is not likely to damage a device (or other components in the circuit). Only two types are used in the projects, and these both have the same case and leadout configuration (see Figure 5). An important point to note here is that transistor leadout diagrams show the base view of the device. In other words, it is shown as it is seen if the leadout wires are towards the viewer. In the component layout diagrams there is insufficient space for the leadout wires to be identified by the full words "base", "emitter", and "collector", and these

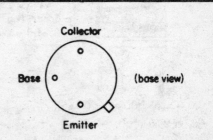

Fig. 5 Leadout details of the BC109C and BC179 devices

12

are therefore abbreviated to "b", "e", and "c" respectively.

Integrated Circuits
Integrated circuits have a wide variety of packages, but here we are only concerned with two types of integrated circuit, the TLO81CP operational amplifier and the LM380N audio power amplifier. The TLO81CP has an 8-pin DIL (dual in line) plastic package, and the LM380N has a 14-pin DIL plastic package. As can be seen from the pinout diagram of Figure 6, the two packages are essentially the same; the 14-pin version simply being an extended version of the 8-pin one. Note that integrated circuit pinout diagrams are top views, and not base views like transistor leadout diagrams. In other words, the device is pictured looking at the side that carries the type number and with the pins pointing away from the viewer.

The only point to watch when connecting one of the integrated circuits is to make sure that it is not plugged in upside-down. Check that the indentation on the top of the package and at one end of the device corresponds properly with the component layout diagram (where this indentation will always be clearly shown).

There are alternative operational amplifier integrated

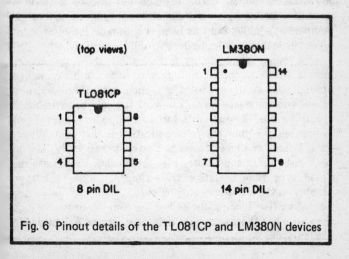

Fig. 6 Pinout details of the TL081CP and LM380N devices

13

circuits that can be used instead of the TLO81CP device incidentally, but only internally compensated BIFET types are suitable, and the standard 741C operational amplifier is not suitable as it will not function properly in some of the projects. Alternative operational amplifier integrated circuits that are suitable are the LF351 and TLO71CP devices. Although some FET operational amplifier devices require special handling precautions, these are the types which have MOSFET input stages, and not the BIFET devices mentioned above which can be handled like any normal semiconductor component without risk of damage. Note that there are no common alternatives to the LM380N device and that the 14-pin version of this device must be used (a few suppliers also offer an 8-pin version).

Diodes

Two types of ordinary diode are used in the projects, the OA90 germanium type and the 1N4148 silicon type. Physically these are very much the same; the OA90 type being somewhat larger than the 1N4148 device. The main point to note about diodes is that they are polarised components and must be connected into circuit the right way round if the circuit is to function properly. The cathode (+) lead of a diode is normally marked by a band around the appropriate end of the component's body, and this band is shown on the component layout diagrams in order to indicate diode polarity.

One minor complication is that there are a few diodes around which for no obvious reason, have the band marked around the wrong end of the component! Therefore, if a circuit which uses diodes fails to work it would be advisable to check the diodes with some sort of component tester if this is possible. Another minor complication is that some diodes have a number of bands marked around their body, and in such cases the manufacturer uses these bands to indicate the diode type number rather than simply marking the type number on the component. In such cases the bands are normally offset towards the end of the component from which the cathode (+) leadout wire emanates. Figure 7 should help to clarify this point.

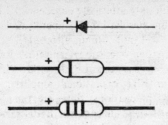

Fig. 7 Diode polarity is shown by a band (or bands) on the component

Two light-emitting diodes (LEDs) are employed in the projects, and these are both small types (3 mm or 0.125 in), but the TIL209 is a red device and the TIL211 is a green LED. Many component suppliers do not use type numbers for LEDs and simply describe them as a LED of a certain colour, diameter and shape (the TIL209 and TIL 211 are both round types incidentally). With most LED circuits, including those described here, from the electrical viewpoint the size, colour, and shape of the LED is not important, and with the exceptions of a few special types such as infra-red and multicolour types any LEDs can be used. For the circuits that use both LEDs it is not even essential to use LEDs of different colours, but a two-colour display will probably be clearer than one having LEDs of the same colour.

There are various ways used to show which LED leadout wire is the anode and which is the cathode, one of the most common being to have one leadout wire shorter than the other as shown in Figure 8. Usually the shorter leadout wire is the cathode one (+), but unfortunately this is not always the case, and sometimes a different method of identification is used. With some LEDs there is no obvious way of telling which leadout wire is which as they seem to be symmetrical! If the manufacturer's or retailer's data is not available, or does not make it clear which leadout wire is which, you can simply try each LED either way round. If a device is wrongly connected

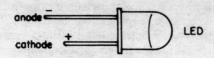

Fig. 8 A common way of showing LED polarity is to have one leadout (usually the cathode) shorter than the other

it will fail to light but is unlikely to sustain any damage, and it will merely be necessary to reverse the polarity of the device in order to make the circuit function correctly.

Potentiometers
These are available in a number of different types, but the circuits in this book require the common carbon type that are available from virtually any electronic component retailer. Wire-wound types are electrically suitable, but are often physically rather large and more expensive and are not recommended. Rotary types are preferable to slider types as the latter are usually much more difficult to mount, and all the component layout diagrams in this book which show a potentiometer assume that a rotary type is used. In these diagrams the potentiometer is shown viewed from the rear (i.e. looking from the opposite side to the spindle and control knob). It is important to connect the potentiometer correctly in most cases as otherwise, for example, advancing a volume control might give a decrease in volume rather than an increase.

Potentiometers are available with a linear law (lin. = linear abbreviated types) or with a logarithmic law (log. types), and circuits will work if the wrong type is used (provided it has the right value of course). However, if we take a volume control as a simple example, a logarithmic type would normally be utilized in this application, and using this type of potentiometer gives an apparently smooth and easily controlled increase in volume as the control is advanced. If a linear type is used there is an apparent sudden increase in volume as the control is advanced from zero, with very little apparent change in volume over the major part of the control's adjustment range. It is possible to set the volume at any desired level, but the volume -level is comparatively difficult to control accurately. Thus it is advisable to use a potentiometer of the type specified in the appropriate components list.

Photocell

The photocell used in the light-activated circuits is an RPY58A which is a small cadmium sulphide photo-resistor, and physically is flat, about 5 mm square, and has the two leadout wires coming from one edge. It looks very much like a small ceramic plate capacitor, in fact.

Like an ordinary resistor, a cadmium sulphide photocell is not a polarised component and can be connected into circuit either way round. The light-sensitive surface of the component is the one having a gold patterned surface, and not the one to which the two leadout wires can be clearly seen to connect.

Ferrite Aerial

The radio receiver projects use a medium-wave ferrite aerial, and a suitable type is the Denco MW5FR. Like all ferrite aerials, this consists of a coil (or coils) of wire on a piece of ferrite. In the case of the MW5FR the piece of ferrite is a rod measuring about 127 mm x 9.5 mm and there are two coils of wire on a paper former which is slipped onto the rod. The two coils are a large (tuned) winding and a smaller (coupling) winding. They are wound using wires of different colours so that it is easy to determine which leadouts come from which winding. The coils are wound using Litz wire (a number of thin enamelled copper wires twisted together and given an overall layer of insulation as well), and the ends of the leadout wires are ready-tinned with solder so that they should fit into the breadboard without too much difficulty.

It is not essential to use the Denco aerial, and the circuits have also been tested using an Ambit MWC2 aerial coil on an Ambit 140 mm X 9.5 mm ferrite rod. However, this aerial coil has tag connections rather than leadout wires, and leads must either be soldered to the tags or connected using small crocodile clips. The circuits should work properly using any other standard medium-wave ferrite aerial provided the aerial coil has the small coupling winding.

. The ferrite aerial can simply be layed on the workbench, or at the rear of the breadboard assembly if a unit along the lines of Figure 2 is constructed. Alternatively, the aerial can be mounted on the breadboard assembly using either a "P" style cable grip capable of taking a 9.5 mm diameter cable (or ferrite rod in this case, of course), or special mounting clips which are available from Ambit International. If the aerial is left loose, bear in mind that ferrite is a very hard and brittle material, and that if the aerial is dropped it is quite likely that the ferrite rod will break. Also bear in mind that the aerial will not operate properly if it is laid on a metal surface and that some plastic laminates used for bench and table tops have a layer of metal foil on their underside.

Switches

Only two types of switches are used in the projects, and there is little chance of confusion since one is a push-button type and the other is a miniature toggle switch (i.e. it is operated via a small lever). The push-button switch must be a push-to-make type and not a push-to-break type, and it must not be a latching type. In other words, the two tags are connected together when the switch is operated, and disconnected when the push button is released. There should be no problem in obtaining a switch of the correct type as these are the most common and cheapest type of push-button switch. Although a miniature toggle switch was used when testing the prototype projects, a standard size toggle switch is also suitable, but a much larger mounting hole will be required (usually about 13 mm or ½ in in diameter). In the components list the toggle switch is specified as an SPST type, and this means a single-pole, single-throw type. In other words, it is just a simple on/off type switch, and switches of this type are sometimes advertised as on/off switches rather than SPST types.

Some of the projects use a relay, and this is a switch that is operated via an electromagnet, and is not operated manually.

The circuits can use any relay having an operating coil with a resistance of about 185 ohms or more, and capable of operating from a 9 volt supply. A type having a fairly high coil resistance has the advantage of a comparatively low battery current drain, and thus gives longer battery life. Most relays operate two or four sets of switch contacts, and these are often of the changeover type rather than simple on/off contacts. A relay of this type is perfectly suitable even if you merely want the relay to switch a single piece of equipment on and off. However, make sure that the voltage and current ratings of the relay are sufficient to control the piece of equipment concerned. Relays do not normally have leadout wires, and the tags of the relay must be connected to the breadboard via suitable soldered or crocodile clip leads.

Loudspeaker

There should be no difficulty in identifying the loudspeaker which will have a diaphragm made from a paper-like substance, and about 50 to 75 mm in diameter (depending on what size loudspeaker you purchase). Apart from the diameter of the loudspeaker, advertisements will also quote an impedance in ohms. The size of the loudspeaker is not of great importance in this case and any miniature type will do, but it is important to use a type having the correct impedance. All the designs require a high-impedance loudspeaker, and any impedance in the range 40 to 80 ohms is suitable. A somewhat higher impedance would be satisfactory, but loudspeakers having an impedance of more than 80 ohms do not seem to be available. Except where noted otherwise, the use of a low-impedance loudspeaker such as an 8-ohm type is not recommended.

Loudspeakers should be treated carefully since the diaphragm is easily damaged, and you should always hold a loudspeaker by the magnet housing at the rear of the component.

CHAPTER 2

THE PROJECTS

In this chapter details of the thirty projects will be provided, and the following will be given for each project:

— Introduction to the project and its applications;
— Circuit description;
— Circuit diagram;
— Component layout diagram;
— Components list;
— Notes on use of project and construction tips.

It is likely that the circuit diagram and circuit description will be of little interest to the complete beginner who will be unfamiliar with even the simplest of electronics theory. However, at some later date, when some theory of electronic components has been learnt, one can always return to these descriptions and diagrams, and perhaps rebuild the circuits as well. For anyone interested in the theory of electronics a number of breadboard projects and circuit descriptions are an ideal way of testing the theory in practice, and in a way that provides fun and enjoyment.

Detailed notes on how to construct the projects on the breadboard will not be given since the layout diagrams are largely self-explanatory, and this would also be largely just reiterating points from the previous chapter. There are just one or two further points which should be kept in mind when breadboarding the projects.

It is not necessary to plug in the components in any special order, but it is best to start with the link wires, transistors, and integrated circuits, and then add the resistors, and other passive components, and finally connect the battery controls, loudspeaker, etc. The link wires are simply short pieces of single-strand wire, and can be pieces of the same wire that is used to wire the breadboard to the controls. There is no need to trim the leadout wires of components to length, and it is in

21

fact unwise to do so as this might result in a component having leadout wires that are too short to enable it to fit into a subsequent component layout. However, if the leadout wires are left full-length be careful to avoid accidental short circuits. When removing an integrated circuit from the board use a small screwdriver (or a proper integrated circuit removal tool) to gently prise the device clear of the breadboard. It is quite likely that if the device is removed by hand one end will pull clear of the board while the other is still in place, and this could result in some of the pins breaking off.

Where necessary, any special setting-up is described in detail, and any special points concerning the construction of the project as a finished and cased unit will be explained.

Project 1 – Simple Audio Power Amplifier

This extremely simple circuit (see Figure 9) provides an output of power of about 200 mW RMS (about equal in volume to a small or medium-size transistor radio) and has an input sensitivity of about 50 mV RMS into 100 k for maximum output. This enables the unit to be fed from a variety of signal sources, such as a crystal or ceramic pick-up, radio tuner, etc. The circuit is primarily intended as a simple one to demonstrate the properties of the LM380N audio-power amplifier device, and it also makes a very useful and inexpensive workshop amplifier if the circuit is built as a proper, cased project.

The LM380N has been a very popular device since it first became available to the home-constructor, and the reasons for this are its good quality output, and the very small number of discrete components needed to turn it into a practical audio amplifier. As we shall see later, it is also a very versatile device that can be used in applications other than audio amplifier ones.

VR1 is the volume control, and the internal circuitry of the LM380N is such that no DC blocking capacitor is needed between the slider of VR1 and the intput of the LM380N (IC1). A DC blocking capacitor is used at the input to VR1 though, so that any DC component that might be present on the input signal is blocked from the input of IC1. IC1 has an internal bias circuit that gives a quiescent output voltage at the output terminal (pin 8) of nominally half the supply voltage. The AC input signal causes the output to swing positive and negative of this quiescent level by about plus and minus 3 volts or so, and this enables a reasonably high output power to be obtained without the output going fully positive or fully negative, and serious distortion being caused by clipping of the output waveform. If a DC component on the input signal was allowed to reach the input of IC1 this would alter the quiescent output voltage of IC1, and could result in the output going almost fully positive or negative. Only a very small output power would then be possible without the signal becoming badly distorted. C1 provides DC blocking at the output so that the loudspeaker only receives the varying output voltage from IC1, and not the quiescent (DC) output voltage which would

23

give a high standing current through the loudspeaker and produce a very high level of current consumption.

The LM380N has a class AB output stage, and this means that the average current consumption of the device (which is around 10 mA) remains virtually constant at low and medium output powers, but increases somewhat at high output powers. This gives reasonable battery economy, and a PP6 or larger 9 volt battery makes a suitable power source. There is some variation in the supply voltage due to variations in the loading on the battery by IC1 as the output power inevitably fluctuates quite rapidly and over a fairly wide range with any practical input signal. This can result in a loss of performance or instability, and decoupling capacitors C2 and C3 are included to prevent either of these occuring. An additional decoupling capacitor can be added from pin 1 of IC1 to the negative supply, and this decouples the supply to the preamplifier stages of the device. This is not normally necessary when the LM380N is employed with a battery supply, and is a facility

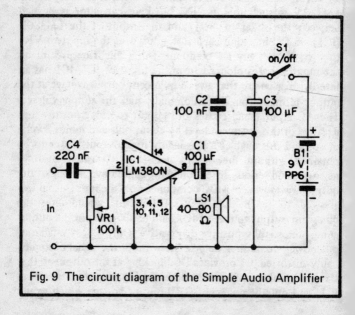

Fig. 9 The circuit diagram of the Simple Audio Amplifier

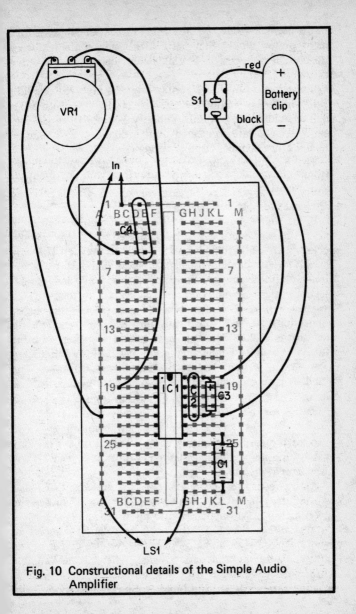

Fig. 10 Constructional details of the Simple Audio
Amplifier

that is normally only required when the device is used with a mains power supply that has a high ripple content. Such a capacitor is not used in any of the circuits in this book that utilize the LM380N device.

Some readers might be confused by the fact that one lead to IC1 in Figure 9 is marked "3, 4, 5, 10, 11, 12". This lead is marked with six pin numbers merely because these six pins are internally interconnected, and a connection to one of them is also a connection to the other five.

The Verobloc component layout for the Audio Power Amplifier is given in Figure 10, and this is so simple that there is very little that can go wrong (remember to fit IC1, C1 and C3 round the right way though).

If the unit is built as a cased project the input leads from the component board should be connected to a two-way audio socket such as a standard or 3.5 mm jack type. The case should ideally be an all-metal type so that it screens the circuitry from stray pick-up of mains hum and similar electrical signals, and the case should be earthed to the negative supply. With most types of audio socket this chassis connection will be automatically provided through the earth lead to the socket. The test leads should use screened cable (the outer braiding connecting to the chassis of the amplifier).

A simple way of testing the breadboard version of the amplifier is to connect a crystal earphone to the input of the circuit. The earphone can then be used in reverse as a sort of crude microphone, although it will only give a fairly low output level and the volume obtained will not be very high. Also, as the earphone lead is not a screened type it is likely that a fair amount of mains hum and other stray pick-up will be evident at the output.

An interesting feature of the LM380N device is that it has two inputs, pin 2 is the non-inverting input and pin 6 is the inverting input. An input signal to pin 6 produces a change in output voltage that is of the opposite polarity, whereas an input to pin 2 gives a change in output voltage that is of the same polarity as the input signal. There is no audible difference between the two, and the fact that the signal is inverted through IC1 if the input at pin 6 is used is not really

26

of any practical importance. The circuit works equally well whichever of the two inputs is used, and this fact can easily be demonstrated in practice. To do so you can try plugging the lead from the slider (centre tag) of VR1 to hole B—23 so that it connects to pin 6 of IC1 and the unit will appear to operate as before. If a link is used to connect hole D—19 to hole D—23 so that both inputs are used, they will tend to cancel out one another and give very little voltage gain!

Components for Project 1 — Simple Audio-Power Amplifier (Fig. 9)

Resistors:
VR1   100 k log. carbon
Capacitors:
C1   100 μf 10 V electrolytic
C2   100 nF polyester (brown, black, yellow, black, red)
C3   100 μF 10 V electrolytic
C4   220 nF polyester (red, red, yellow, black, red)
Semiconductor:
IC1   LM380N
Switch:
S1   SPST miniature toggle type
Battery:
B1   PP6 size 9 volt and connector to suit
Loudspeaker:
LS1   Miniature type having an impedance in the range 40 to 80 ohms
Miscellaneous:
Verobloc
Control knob
Wire

Project 2 – Telephone Amplifier

This is a simple device which can be used to boost the output of a telephone to loudspeaker volume so that a number of people can follow a telephone conversation, and no direct connection to the telephone is needed. The audio signal is picked up using a special coil that is fitted to the base part of the telephone using a built-in rubber suction cup. In effect, the pick-up coil and a component within the telephone form a

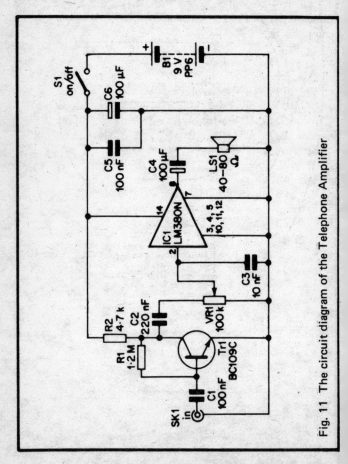

Fig. 11 The circuit diagram of the Telephone Amplifier

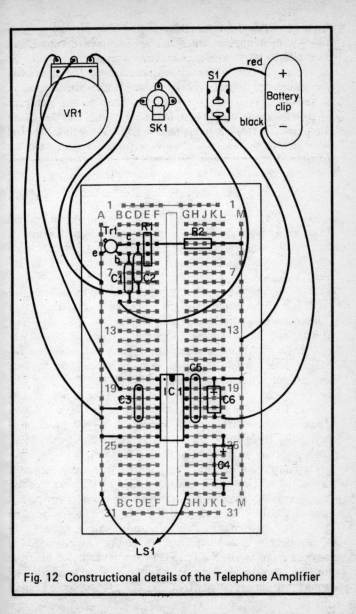

Fig. 12 Constructional details of the Telephone Amplifier

transformer, and give the required audio signal. The unit has other possible applications such as an intercom or baby alarm, as explained later.

Figure 11 shows the circuit diagram of the Telephone Amplifier and Figure 12 gives the breadboard component layout.

The output circuitry of the unit is basically the same as the amplifier described in the previous section of this book. The only difference is the addition of a capacitor (C3) from the input of IC1 to the negative supply rail. The purpose of this capacitor is to reduce the upper audio response of the circuit, and this gives an improved signal to noise ratio (i.e. less background "hiss") without reducing intelligibility.

The voltage gain of the LM380N device is set by an internal negative feedback network at approximately 34 dB (50 times), and this is inadequate to give a reasonably loud output since the pick-up coil provides only a very small signal level. A high-gain common-emitter amplifier based on Tr1 is therefore used to boost the gain to a suitably high level, and the voltage gain of Tr1 is in the region of 40 dB (100 times). This stage uses a conventional configuration with R2 as the collector load resistor and R1 biasing the circuit. C1 provides DC blocking at the input, and is necessary as the pick-up coil has a low DC resistance and would otherwise virtually short-circuit the base terminal of Tr1 to the negative supply rail.

The input signal is inverted through Tr1, but not through IC1 so that the input and output of the amplifier are out-of-phase. Stray feedback at high frequencies is unlikely to cause instability therefore, despite the very high gain of the circuit, since such feedback will be of the negative variety.

If you decide to build this one as a permanent project it would be advisable to use a metal case so that the sensitive input circuitry is screened. The telephone pick-up coil is placed on the base section of the telephone in the position that gives the best signal pick-up, and it will be necessary to experiment a little here. Note that if the volume control is advanced too far, or the telephone handset is placed too close to LS1, acoustic feedback will cause oscillation and a howling sound will be produced from LS1. Try to keep the handset and LS1 reasonably well separated.

The amplifier is suitable for other applications where only a low input signal level is available (medium- and high-level signals would overload the input stage and cause severe distortion), and with suitable switching the circuit could be used as an intercom. The input would then be fed from a high-impedance loudspeaker of the same type as used for LS1, and this would operate in reverse as a sort of moving-coil microphone. To permit communications in the opposite direction, LS1 would be connected to the input to act as the microphone and the other loudspeaker would be fed from the output of the amplifier. Figure 13 shows the switching necessary to achieve this, and the switch used should be a biased type which automatically switches to the "receive" position when released. The slave station can then call the main one by operating push-button switch S2 so that power from the additional battery is connected to the amplifier, and then talking into the microphone so that the attention of any-one at the main station then operates the on/off switch and the send/receive switch (S3), and S2 can be released. The main station calls the slave one simply by setting S1 to the "on" position, S3 to the "send" position, and talking into the microphone.

The circuit can be used as a baby alarm simply by feeding the input from a high-impedance loudspeaker (used as a micro-phone) or a low-impedance dynamic microphone (i.e. the type used with inexpensive cassette recorders). However, the current consumption of the unit is high enough to make battery operation for long periods of time rather expensive unless rechargeable NiCad cells are used.

Components for Project 2 – Telephone Amplifier (Fig. 11)
  Resistors: all 1/3 watt 5% (10% over 1 M)
R1   1.2 M (brown, red, green, silver)
R2   4.7 k (yellow, violet, red, gold)
VR1   100 k log. carbon
  Capacitors:
C1   100 nF polyester (brown, black, yellow, black, red)
C2   220 nF polyester (red, red, yellow, black, red)

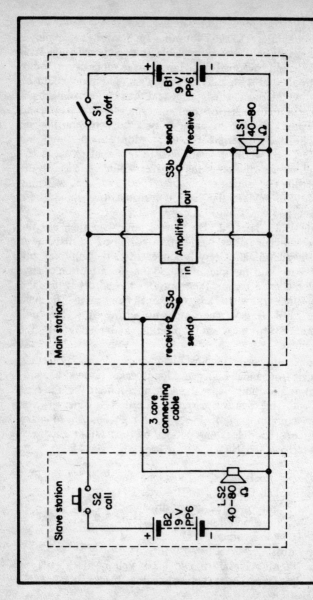

Fig. 13 A simple method of using the Telephone Amplifier in an intercom system

32

C3   10 nF polyester (brown, black, orange, black, red)
C4   100 μF 10 V electrolytic
C5   100 nF polyester (brown, black, yellow, black, red)
C6   100 μF 10 V electrolytic

Semiconductors:

IC1   LM380N
Tr1   BC109C

Switch:

S1   SPST miniature toggle type

Battery:

B1   PP6 size 9 volt and connector to suit

Loudspeaker:

LS1   Miniature type having an impedance in the range 40 to 80 ohms

Socket:

SK1 3.5 mm jack type

Miscellaneous:

Verobloc
Control knob
Telephone pick-up coil
Wire

Project 3 — Light-Activated Switch

Light-activated switches have applications in fields such as burglar-alarm systems and automatic control systems. They also make interesting projects for the electronics experimenter. The circuit diagram shown in Figure 14 is for a switch of the type that activates a relay when the light level received by the light sensor rises above a certain threshold level, and switches off again when the light level falls back below the threshold level. The component layout and wiring diagram for the Light-Activated Switch appears in Figure 15.

The relay coil is driven from the collector of Tr1, and the relay will be activated if Tr1 is switched on by a suitable base-current and voltage. The voltage and current available at the base of Tr1 is dependent on two main factors, the resistance provided by PCC1, and the setting of VR1. If VR1 is set at maximum value PCC1 needs to have a resistance of about 100 k or less in order to bias Tr1 into conduction and activate the relay. In total darkness PCC1 has a resistance of 200 k or more, but only a very low light level is sufficient to reduce its

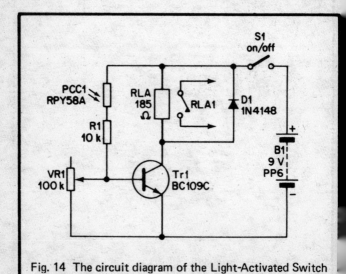

Fig. 14 The circuit diagram of the Light-Activated Switch

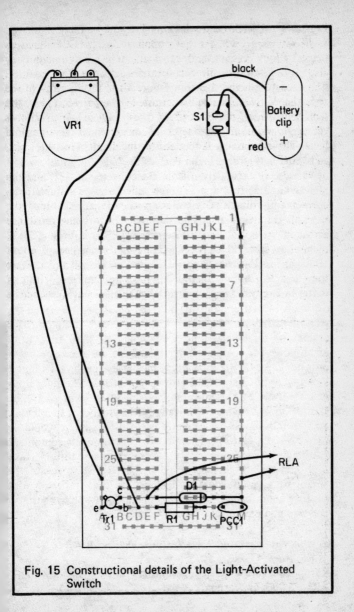

Fig. 15 Constructional details of the Light-Activated Switch

resistance sufficiently to switch on Tr1 and the relay.

If VR1 is set for a lower resistance level, PCC1 needs to exhibit a lower resistance in order to bias Tr1 into conduction, and the sensitivity of the circuit is reduced since PCC1 must be subjected to a higher light level in order to produce this lower resistance. If VR1 is steadily adjusted lower in resistance, the sensitivity of the circuit is progressively reduced. With VR1 at virtually minimum resistance even an extremely high level of light will be insufficient to operate the circuit. Thus VR1 acts as a sensitivity control, and enables the light-threshold level to be varied over extremely wide limits.

D1 might at first appear to be superfluous, but it must be borne in mind that a relay coil is a highly inductive component, and this can result in a high reverse voltage being generated across the relay coil as it is de-energised. The purpose of D1 is to suppress this voltage pulse and prevent it from damaging Tr1.

A pair of normally-open relay contacts are used to control some ancillary item of equipment, and this equipment will be switched on and off in sympathy with the relay. The unit is capable of controlling mains-powered equipment provided the relay used has a high enough contact voltage rating, but for reasons of safety the unit should only be used to control mains-powered equipment if it is built as a proper cased project. The case must be a type having a screw-on lid and not a clip-on type that would give easy access to the dangerous mains wiring. The negative supply rail of the unit should be earthed to the mains earth lead, and any exposed metalwork on the unit should be similarly earthed. Beginners would be well advised not to use the unit to control mains equipment until they have gained the necessary experience to undertake this safely. Until then it would be better just to regard the circuit as a simple one to demonstrate the properties of a photocell, or to use the relay to operate low-voltage battery-powered equipment.

Components for Project 3 – Light-Activated Switch (Fig. 14)
   Resistors: 1/3 watt 5%
R1   10 k (brown, black, orange, gold)
VR1   100 k lin. carbon

Semiconductors:
Tr1   BC109C
D1   1N4148
    Photocell:
PCC1 RPY58A
    Switch:
S1   SPST miniature toggle type
    Relay:
RLA   6/12 volt coil having a resistance of 185 ohms or more,
        and contacts of appropriate type and adequate rating.
    Battery:
B1   PP6 size 9-volt and connector to suit
    Miscellaneous:
Verobloc
Control knob
Wire

Project 4 – Dark-Activated Switch

The circuit diagram of the Dark-Activated Switch is given in Figure 16, and the breadboard component layout is shown in Figure 17.

This circuit is a modified version of the previous one, and basically VR1 and PCC1 have been swopped over. Thus, in this circuit a base current is allowed to flow into Tr1 and switch the device on when PCC1 is in darkness and has a high resistance. Under bright conditions PCC1 has a low resistance and effectively short-circuits the base of Tr1 to earth and cuts it off. With VR1 at maximum resistance PCC1 will cut off Tr1 unless a very low level of light is present, but with VR1 at minimum resistance the light threshold is raised considerably, and VR1 acts as a sensitivity control much as it did in the circuit of Figure 14. Also in common with the previous circuit, R1 is included to ensure that an excessive base current cannot flow into the base of Tr1.

Of course, if any of the light-sensitive circuits described in this book are constructed as permanent cased projects, the

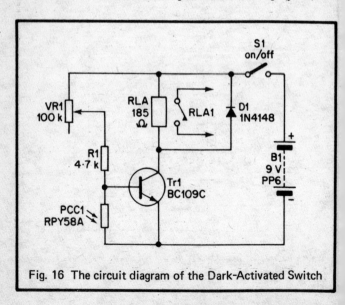

Fig. 16 The circuit diagram of the Dark-Activated Switch

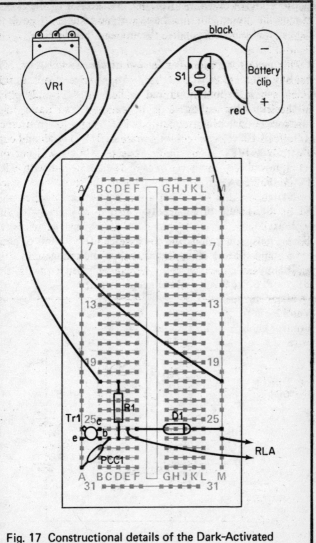

Fig. 17 Constructional details of the Dark-Activated
Switch

photocell must either be fitted on the exterior of the case, or it must be mounted inside the case behind a hole drilled in the case so that it can respond to the ambient light level.

Components for Project 4 – Dark-Activated Switch (Fig. 16)
Resistors: 1/3 watt 5%
R1   4.7 k (yellow, violet, red, gold)
VR1   100 k lin. carbon
Semiconductors:
Tr1   BC109C
D1   1N4148
Photocell:
PCC1   RPY58A
Switch:
S1   SPST miniature toggle type
Relay:
RLA   6/12 volt coil having a resistance of 185 ohms or more, and contacts of appropriate type and rating.
Battery:
B1   PP6 size 9 volt and connector to suit
Miscellaneous:
Verobloc
Control knob
Wire

Project 5 – Light Alarm

This circuit produces an audio tone if the photocell is subjected to a reasonably high level of light (normal daylight and artifical room lighting are sufficient to operate the circuit). The unit could be used as a simple burglar deterrent, and it would then be placed in a cupboard or a drawer, and would produce the alarm signal if the cupboard or drawer was opened by a burglar, hopefully unnerving him or her sufficiently to make them leave the premises immediately. It could also be used in a medicine cupboard to sound a warning if a small child should somehow manage to open the cupboard. In this application the on/off switch should be fitted somewhere on the outside of the cupboard (preferably out of sight on top of the cupboard where a small child would be unable to reach it and probably be unaware of its existence) so that the alarm could be switched off before opening the cupboard, and switched on again after it has been closed. The alarm might otherwise attract the attention of a small child.

The circuit is similar to the Light-Activated Switch circuit described earlier, but instead of driving a relay the switching transistor drives an audio alarm circuit. Also, a fixed resistor has been used across the base - emitter terminals of the switching transistor so that the sensitivity of the circuit is preset. However, R4 can be raised somewhat in value if increased sensitivity is required. Alternatively, it can be replaced with a 100 k linear potentiometer if variable sensitivity is required.

The audio-alarm generator uses an LM380N (IC1) in a simple audio-oscillator circuit, and driving high-impedance loudspeaker LS1 via coupling capacitor C3. It is a simple matter to get a non-inverting amplifier having a fairly high gain to oscillate, and it is merely necessary to provide AC coupling from the output to the input. Provided the losses through this coupling are less than the voltage gain provided by the amplifier this will give sufficient positive feedback to sustain oscillation.

The values for R1, R2, and C2 shown in the circuit diagram (Figure 18) give considerably more feedback than is needed to just sustain oscillation, and the circuit oscillates strongly pro-

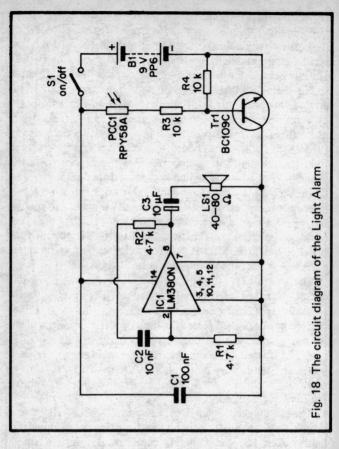

Fig. 18 The circuit diagram of the Light Alarm

ducing a roughly squarewave output at a frequency in the region of 1 kHz.

The breadboard component layout for the Light Alarm is shown in Figure 19.

Components for Project 5 – Light Alarm (Fig. 18)
    Resistors: all 1/3 watt 5%
R1   4.7 k (yellow, violet, red, gold)
R2   4.7 k (yellow, violet, red, gold)

42

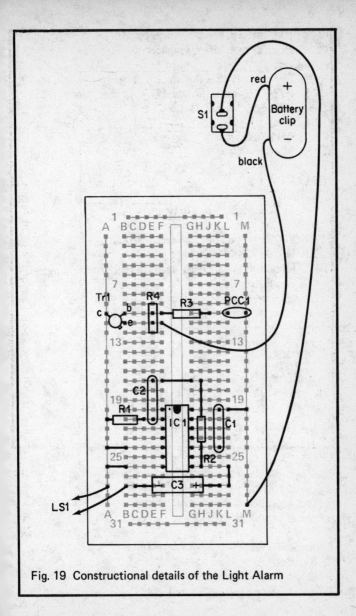

Fig. 19 Constructional details of the Light Alarm

R3   10 k (brown, black, orange, gold)
R4   10 k (brown, black, oragne, gold)
   Capacitors:
C1   100 nF polyester (brown, black, yellow, black, red)
C2   10 nF polyester (brown, black, orange, black, red)
C3   10 μ F 25 V electrolytic
   Semiconductors:
IC1   LM380N
Tr1   BC109C
   Photocell:
PCC1   RPY58A
   Switch:
S1   SPST miniature toggle type
   Battery:
B1   PP6 size 9 volt and connector to suit
   Loudspeaker:
LS1   Miniature type having an impedance in the range 40 to 80 ohms
   Miscellaneous:
Verobloc
Wire

Project 6 — Dark-Activated Alarm

This circuit is similar to the one just described, but it operates an audible alarm if the light intensity received by the photocell falls below a certain threshold level, rather than if it exceeds the threshold level. A possible application for the unit is as a lighting-up-time reminder for a car, and the circuit will operate properly from a 12-volt car battery instead of a 9-volt PP6 size battery.

As can be seen from the circuit diagram of the unit which appears in Figure 20, it is basically the same as the Dark-Activated Switch project described earlier, but the switching transistor drives an audio-alarm circuit rather than a relay. The alarm generator is exactly the same as the one used in the Light Alarm project. VR1 is used to set the light threshold at which the alarm begins to sound, as was the case with the Dark-Activated Switch project.

Figure 21 gives the breadboard component layout for the Dark-Activated Alarm project. Incidentally, it is possible to alter the note produced by the alarm-generator circuit; an increase in the value of R1, R2, or C2 (or more than one of these) producing a reduction in pitch, and vice versa.

Components for Project 6 — Dark-Activated Alarm (Fig. 20)

Resistors: all 1/3 watt 5%

R1   4.7 k (yellow, violet, red, gold)
R2   4.7 k (yellow, violet, red, gold)
R3   10 k (brown, black, orange, gold)
VR1   100 k lin. carbon

Capacitors:

C1   100 nF polyester (brown, black, yellow, black, red)
C2   10 nF polyester (brown, black, orange, black, red)
C3   10 μF 25 V electrolytic

Semiconductors:

IC1   LM380N
Tr1   BC109C

Photocell:

PCC1 RPY58A

Switch:

S1   SPST miniature toggle type

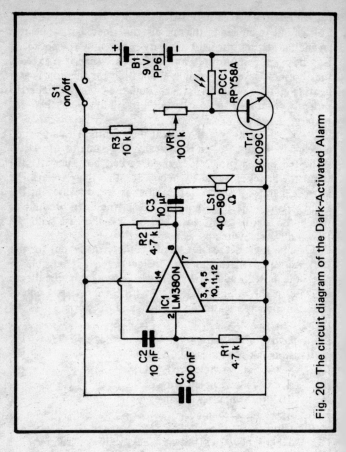

Fig. 20 The circuit diagram of the Dark-Activated Alarm

Battery:
B1   PP6 size 9 volt and connector to suit
    Loudspeaker:
LS1   Miniature type having an impedance in the range of 40
        to 80 ohms
    Miscellaneous:
Verobloc
Control Knob
Wire

46

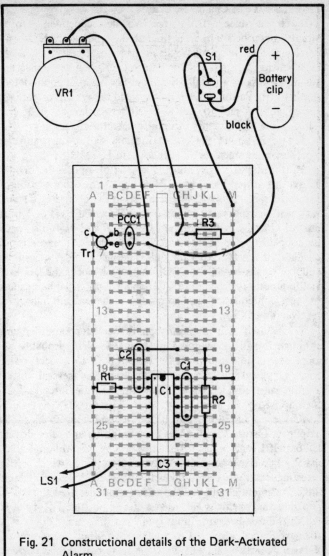

Fig. 21 Constructional details of the Dark-Activated Alarm

Project 7 – Light Change Switch

This circuit differs from the two light-dependent switch circuits described earlier in that it does not activate at any particular light level, but instead activates a relay if a fairly rapid change in light level is detected. A possible application for the unit is in a burglar-alarm system where it could detect the light from a torch beam as it crossed the sensor, or perhaps the shadow of an intruder as it fell across the sensor. It also has possible uses in other proximity-detector applications.

Figure 22 shows the circuit diagram of the unit, and the Verobloc component layout is shown in Figure 23.

Photocell PCC1 is connected as part of a potential divider across the supply lines, with R1 acting as the other section of the divider. The voltage at the junction of R1 and PCC1 will vary with changes in the light level received by PCC1, but normal changes in the ambient light level will be too slow to be coupled by C1 to the base of Tr1. However, more rapid changes, of the type that the unit is designed to detect, will be coupled to the base of Tr1. Of course, C1 blocks the DC level at the junction of R1 and PCC1, and the potential here is not of great consequence (and so neither is the ambient light level received by PCC1).

Tr1 is used as a high-gain common-emitter amplifier and although it will receive an input signal level of probably no more than a few millivolts, the output at Tr1's collector will have a typical peak-to-peak voltage-swing of several volts. This signal is coupled by C2 to a simple rectifier circuit which is comprised of D1 and D2.

IC1 is an LM380N, but it is not used here as an audio amplifier. Instead it is used as a DC amplifier and relay driver. Pin 6 of IC1 is given a small positive bias by R5, while R4 gives pin 2 a negative bias. The positive bias to Pin 6 (which is the inverting input) therefore takes the output fully negative, and under quiescent conditions the relay is not energised.

When the circuit is activated a strong positive DC signal is fed to the non-inverting input (pin 2) of IC1, and if this bias is stronger than the one fed to the inverting input, the output of IC1 goes positive and energises the relay coil. A bias current then flows from the output of IC1 to the non-inverting input by way of R6, D4, and D3, and this bias current holds the circuit with IC1's output high and the relay latched in the on state. The reason for including D3 and D4 in the feedback circuit is that the output of IC1 is not fully negative under standby conditions, and the voltage drop through D3 and D4 ensures that the feedback circuit does not provide pin 2 with a large enough positive bias to spuriously trigger the circuit.

If S1 is operated, pin 2 of IC1 is taken to the negative supply voltage again and the circuit is reset to its original state with the relay switched off. It may be found that the circuit triggers at switch-on, and this is quite likely in fact. However, this is not easily avoidable, and is of little importance since it is merely necessary to reset the circuit using S1 if it should prove to be necessary.

An important point to bear in mind about this circuit is that unlike the previous circuits which consume typically only a fraction of a milliamp under quiescent conditions and can be economically run for long periods from a PP6 or larger size 9-volt battery, this one consumes around 11 mA and should be run from NiCad cells if it will be left operating for long periods of time.

Components for Project 7 – Light Change Switch (Fig. 22)
    Resistors: all 1/3 watt 5% (10% over 1 M)
R1   1 k (brown, black, red, gold)
R2   2.7 M (red. violet, green, silver)
R3   4.7 k (yellow, violet, red, gold)
R4   100 k (brown, black, yellow, gold)
R5   1 M (brown, black, green, gold)
R6   33 k (orange, orange, orange, gold)
    Capacitors:
C1   220 nF polyester (red, red, yellow, black, red)
C2   33 μF 10 V tantalum bead
C3   100 nF polyester (brown, black, yellow, black, red)
    Semiconductors:
IC1   LM380N
Tr1   BC109C
D1   OA90
D2   OA90

49

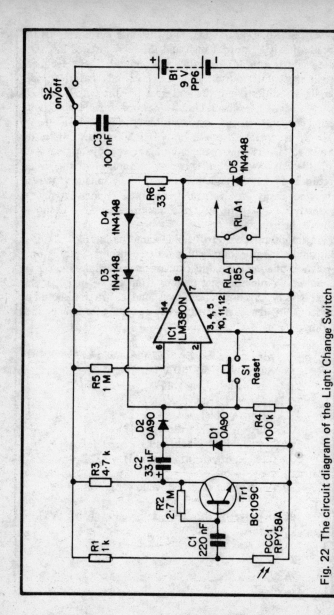

Fig. 22 The circuit diagram of the Light Change Switch

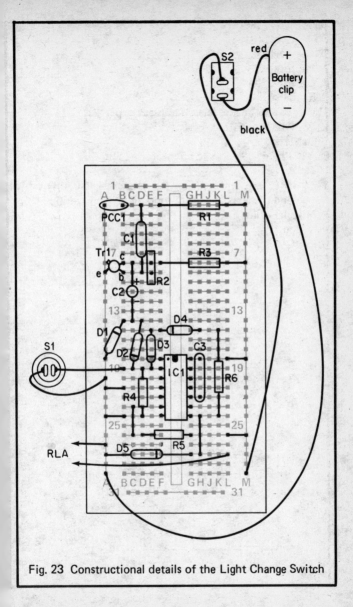

Fig. 23 Constructional details of the Light Change Switch

51

D3   1N4148
D4   1N4148
D5   1N4148
  Photocell:
PCC1   RPY58A
  Switches:
S1   Push-to-make, release-to-break type
S2   SPST miniature toggle type
  Battery:
B1   PP6 size 9 volt and connector to suit
  Relay:
RLA   6/12 volt coil having a resistance of 185 ohms or more
        and contacts of the appropriate type and rating
  Miscellaneous:
Verobloc
Wire

Project 8 – One-Second Timer

This very simple circuit simply pulses on a LED indicator-light briefly at one second intervals, and is suitable for use as a simple photographic timer for timing enlarger 'exposures, or long exposures using a camera with the shutter set on "B" or "T". There are probably many other applications for a simple timer of this type.

Refer to Figure 24 for the circuit diagram of the One-Second Timer, and to Figure 25 for the Verobloc component layout.

The circuit is based on a TL081CP operational-amplifier integrated circuit, but this device is really used here as a voltage comparator. If the non-inverting input (pin 3) is taken to a higher voltage than the inverting input (pin 2) the output goes high (i.e. it assumes a voltage nearly equal to the positive supply voltage). If the comparative input states are reversed the output at pin 6 goes low (i.e. a low voltage of only about one volt or so).

R1 and R2 bias the non-inverting input to half the supply voltage, but R3 and VR1 will actually alter this voltage by shunting R1 if IC1's output is high, or R2 if it is low. C2 will be uncharged at switch on so that the inverting input is taken to the negative supply potential, and the output will go high since the non-inverting input must be at a higher voltage than the inverting one. VR1 and R3 therefore raise the voltage fed to the non-inverting input.

C2 now charges from IC1's output via R4 and R5, and the charge voltage soon exceeds the voltage at the non-inverting input. The output then triggers to the low state and the voltage at the non-inverting input is reduced. C2 now discharges through D1, R5, and the output circuitry of IC1. As D1 bypasses high value resistor R4 during the discharge half-cycle, C2 discharges much faster than it charges. The charge voltage therefore soon drops below the voltage at the non-inverting input and the output triggers to the high state again. C2 then commences charging once more, taking the circuit back to its original state.

Thus the unit oscillates continuously with C2 charging and discharging, and the frequency of oscillation is controlled by

VR1. With VR1 at maximum resistance the change in voltage at the non-inverting input as IC1's output changes state is quite small, and the frequency of operation is relatively high since the charge voltage on C2 has to change very little between output transitions. With VR1 at minimum value the voltage fed to the non-inverting input changes very considerably, and the charge on C2 has to change a great deal to produce the changes in output state. This slows up the circuit action and gives a relatively low operating frequency. In practice, VR1 is adjusted to give an operating frequency of one Hertz. D2 is briefly flashed during the brief periods that IC1's output goes low, and VR1 is simply adjusted by trial and error to give one flash per second using a timepiece which gives seconds-indication as a reference against which the unit is calibrated.

It is important to note that when first switched on there

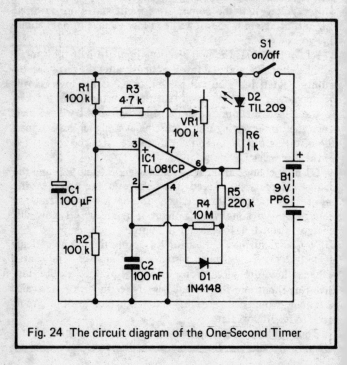

Fig. 24 The circuit diagram of the One-Second Timer

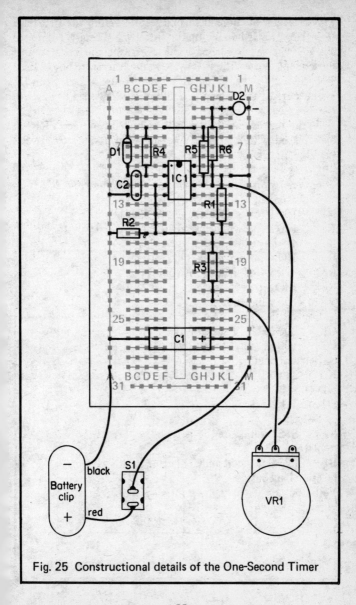

Fig. 25 Constructional details of the One-Second Timer

will be a gap of more than one second before the first flash from D2. This is because on the first cycle C2 starts from zero charge, whereas it retains some charge at the beginning of subsequent cycles. The first cycle should therefore not be used as part of a timing period. It is easier to use a flash from D2 as the start of the timing period, rather than when S1 is set to the on-period anyway.

If the unit is constructed as a permanent project VR1 can be replaced with a preset type, and even a small (0.1 watt) type is suitable.

Components for Project 8 – One-Second Timer (Fig. 24)
Resistors: all 1/3 watt 5% (10% over 1 M)

R1	100 k (brown, black, yellow, gold)
R2	100 k (brown, black, yellow, gold)
R3	4.7 k (yellow, violet, red, gold)
R4	10 M (brown, black, blue, silver)
R5	220 k (red, red, yellow, gold)
R6	1 k (brown, black, red, gold)
VR1	100 k lin. carbon

Capacitors:

C1	100 μF 10 V electrolytic
C2	100 nF polyester (brown, black, yellow, black, red)

Semiconductors:

IC1	TLO81CP
D1	1N4148
D2	TIL209

Switch:

S1	SPST miniature toggle type

Battery:

B1	PP6 size 9 volt and connector to suit

Miscellaneous:
Verobloc
Wire

Project 9 – Metronome

The circuit diagram of the Metronome is shown in Figure 26, and this has obvious similarities with the One-Second Timer project just described. In fact, IC1 is used in what is basically the same oscillator circuit, but the component values have been modified to give a frequency range which is appropriate to this application. VR1 gives about 30 beats per minute at minimum value, rising to around 300 beats per minute at maximum value, but due to the component tolerances these figures are only approximate. However, the unit should give any beat rate that is likely to be needed in practice, and the range covered has purposely been made slightly wider than is really necessary in order to allow for the effects of component tolerances. The unit provides both an audible and a visual indication of the beat.

A small but significant difference between the One-Second Timer and Metronome circuits is the polarity of D1 in each circuit. With the polarity used in the One-Second Timer the output of the oscillator is high for the majority of the time, and low for only very brief periods. With the polarity used in the Metronome the opposite effect is obtained with the output pulses being brief positive ones. LED indicator D2 in the Metronome unit is still briefly flashed on since it is connected from the output of IC1 to the negative supply line, rather than to the positive supply line, as in the One-Second Timer unit.

A normal (mechanical) metronome does not just give a visual indication of the beat rate, but it also gives an audible indication in the form of a series of "clicking" sounds. In this circuit a simulation of this is provided by using the brief output pulses to drive a loudspeaker (LS1). IC1 is not able to provide the fairly high current needed in order to drive the loudspeaker at good volume, and Tr1 is therefore used as an emitter-follower stage which gives the necessary current amplification between IC1 and LS1. R7 and R3 are the current-limiting resistance for D2, and together with D2 they also reduce the voltage drive to Tr1 slightly so that an excessive current cannot be passed through Tr1 during the output pulses.

The Verobloc component layout for the Metronome is

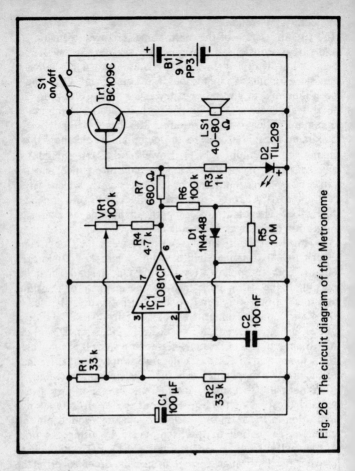

Fig. 26 The circuit diagram of the Metronome

shown in Figure 27.

If the unit is constructed as a permanent project VR1 should be fitted with a large pointer knob, and a scale calibrated in beats per minute can be marked around this. The calibration points are found by trial and error, and the best rate is measured simply by counting the number of beat indications produced in a 1-minute period (or perhaps the number in a 20-second period and then multiplying this figure by 3 in order to

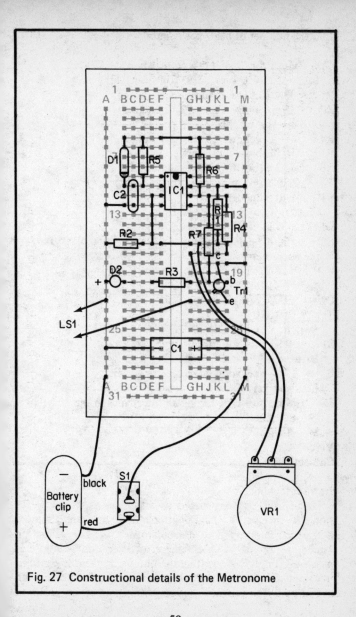

Fig. 27 Constructional details of the Metronome

find the number of beats per minute).

Components for Project 9 – Metronome (Fig. 26)
   Resistors: all 1/3 watt 5% (10% over 1 M)

R1	33 k (orange, orange, orange, gold)
R2	33 k (orange, orange, orange, gold)
R3	1 k (brown, black, red, gold)
R4	4.7 k (yellow, violet, red, gold)
R5	10 M (brown, black, blue, silver)
R6	100 k (brown, black, yellow, gold)
R7	680 ohms (blue, grey, brown, gold)
VR1	100 k lin. carbon

   Capacitors:

C1	100 μf 10 V electrolytic
C2	100 nF polyester (brown, black, yellow, black, red)

   Semiconductors:

IC1	TLO81CP
D1	1N4148
D2	TIL209 (0.125 in red LED)
Tr1	BC109C

   Switch:

S1   SPST miniature toggle type
   Battery:
B1   PP6 size 9 volt and connector to suit
   Loudspeaker:
LS1   Miniature type having an impedance in the range 40 to
       80 ohms
   Miscellaneous:
Verobloc
Control knob
Wire

Project 10 — "Heads" Or "Tails"

This circuit electronically simulates the tossing of a coin, and it is operated by briefly depressing a push-button switch. While the switch is depressed two LED indicators both light up, but only one will remain on when the switch is released. There is no way of predetermining which LED will be the one that remains switched on when the switch is released, and there is no bias to one or other of the LEDs. Thus, by designating one LED "heads" and the other LED "tails", the unit gives the required simulation of a coin being tossed.

The circuit diagram of the "Heads"Or "Tails" unit is shown in Figure 28, and the Verobloc component layout appears in Figure 29.

The circuit of the unit uses an oscillator of the same basic type as the oscillators used in the two previous projects. However, an important and essential difference is that it does not use a diode in the charge/discharge circuit for the timing capacitor. This means that there is no difference between the charge and discharge times, and that the output of the oscillator spends equal amounts of time in the high and low states.

Two LED indicators are driven from the output of IC1, but they are driven out-of-phase. In other words, when IC1's output is high D2 will be switched on, and D1 will be turned off. With IC1's output low it is D2 that becomes switched off and D1 that is switched on. R5 and R6 are the current-limiting resistors for the two LEDs, and R7 plus R8 ensure that the voltage across whichever LED is in the off state is sufficiently low to cause that LED to fully switch off and not visibly glow.

The oscillator will only function properly when S1 is operated, since there is otherwise no charge or discharge path through R4 and the open circuit S1. When the circuit does oscillate the frequency of operation is a few hundred Hertz, and the switching action of D1 and D2 is too fast to be perceived properly by a human observer. Thus rather than flashing, the two LEDs seem to be alight continuously, but as each one is switched off for 50% of the time the average current fed to each LED is only half the normal level and the LEDs appear to be less bright than normal.

61

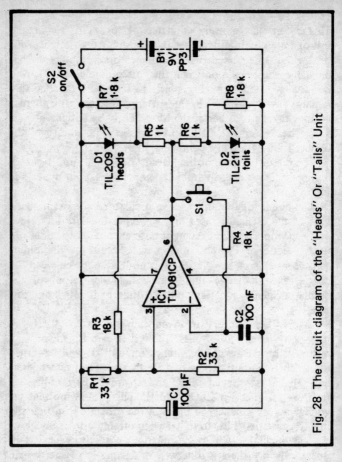

Fig. 28 The circuit diagram of the "Heads" Or "Tails" Unit

When S1 is released C2 is no longer able to charge or discharge through R4 and the output circuitry of IC1, and the input voltage to the inverting input of IC1 remains at whatever level it happened to be at the instant that the contacts of S1 went open-circuit. Thus the output of IC1 stays in whatever state it happened to be in at this instant, and the appropriate LED indicator remains switched on. There is no way of telling in advance which LED this will be, and each LED stands an

62

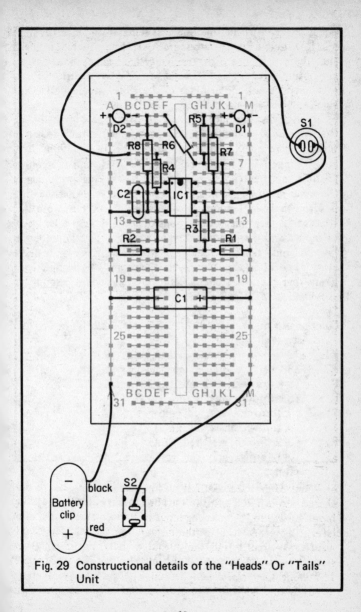

Fig. 29 Constructional details of the "Heads" Or "Tails" Unit

equal chance of being the one that remains on since the high and low times of IC1's output are equal. In practice, it is likely that there will be a slight inequality here since, for example, the output circuitry of IC1 is not perfectly symmetrical. However, any bias to one or other of the LEDs should be far too small to be of any significance.

When trying the unit in practice do not be surprised if at first one LED seems to be dominant, and the unit does not seem to give a truly random output. This is something that could happen when actually tossing a coin, and it is quite possible that tossing a coin six times, for instance, would give the same result all six times. In order to be sure that the unit is giving a truly random answer it is necessary to note the results of a great many operations of the unit (say a hundred or more), and there should then be a roughly equal number of "heads" and "tails". Of course, if the same answer is obtained every time after about a dozen operations of the unit it is likely that there is a circuit fault, and the wiring should be checked.

Components for Project 10 – "Heads" Or "Tails" (Fig. 28)
Resistors: all 1/3 watt 5%

R1	33 k (orange, orange, orange, gold)
R2	33 k (orange, orange, orange, gold)
R3	18 k (brown, grey, orange, gold)
R4	18 k (brown, grey, orange, gold)
R5	1 k (brown, black, red, gold)
R6	1 k (brown, black, red, gold)
R7	1.8 k (brown, grey, red, gold)
R8	1.8 k (brown, grey, red, gold)

Capacitors:

C1	100 μF 10 V electrolytic
C2	100 nF polyester (brown, black, yellow, black, red)

Semiconductors:

IC1	TLO81CP
D1	TIL209 (0.125 in red LED)
D2	TIL211 (0.125 in green LED)

Switches:

S1	Push-to-make, release-to-break type

S2   SPST miniature toggle type
   Battery:
B1   PP6 size 9 volt and connector to suit
   Miscellaneous:
Verobloc
Wire

Project 11 — 4-60 Second Timer

This simple electronic timer switches on a LED indicator between 4 and 60 seconds after switch-on. The time delay is continuously adjustable between these limits. Apart from demonstrating capacitor—resistor time constants, the unit has possible practical applications, and it could, for example, be used as a games timer.

The circuit diagram of the timer unit is shown in Figure 30, and the Verobloc component layout is given in Figure 31.

LED indicator D1 is driven from the output of IC1 by way of current-limiting resistor R3. D1 will be switched off when ICI's output is high, and switched on when ICI's output is low. At switch-on IC1's inverting input will be taken to the negative supply-rail potential since C1 will not have any charge initially, but the non-inverting input will receive a positive bias

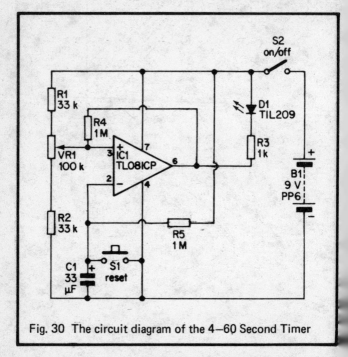

Fig. 30 The circuit diagram of the 4—60 Second Timer

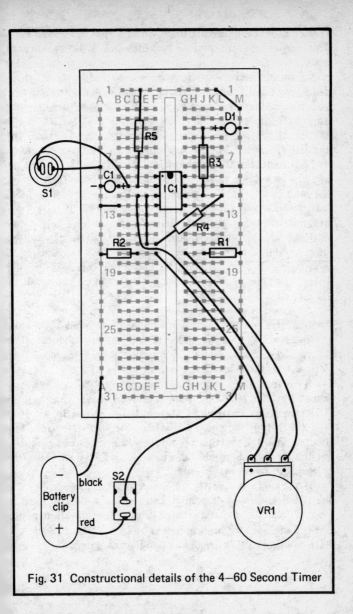

Fig. 31 Constructional details of the 4–60 Second Timer

from the potential divider chain formed by R1, VR1, and R2. The output of VR1 therefore goes high and D1 is not switched on.

C1 immediately starts to charge from the positive supply rail by way of R5, and the charge potential on C1 rises steadily. At some point the charge on C1 will be higher than the bias voltage fed to the non-inverting input, and at this stage the output of IC1 will go low and D1 will light up. The length of time it takes for this to happen depends on a number of factors, including the values of R5 and C1. The time taken for the charge voltage to reach 63% of the supply voltage is 1 CR seconds (with C in μF and R in megohms), and after 5 CR seconds the charge potential is more than 99% of the supply voltage. With the specified values for R5 and C1 this means that the charge on C1 will reach 63% of the supply voltage after a nominal period of 33 seconds, and if VR1 is adjusted to give a potential equal to 63% of the supply voltage at the non-inverting input of IC1 the delay time of the circuit will be 33 seconds.

Adjusting VR1 for a higher voltage gives a greater delay time with a maximum of about 60 seconds being attainable. A lower voltage at the slider of VR1 gives a reduced time delay down to a minimum of approximately 4 seconds. Thus VR1 acts as the delay time control.

R4 is included to give a small amount of DC positive feedback over IC1, and this simply ensures that as the charge on C1 starts to go above the voltage at the non-inverting input of IC1 the output switches rapidly from the high state to the low one so that D1 switches on abruptly, and does not gradually switch on (which would be an ambiguous way of indicating the end of the timing period).

If the timer is constructed as a permanent project VR1 can be fitted with a large pointer knob and a scale calibrated in seconds can be marked around this. The calibration points must be found by empirical means, and note that the scale will be non-linear as C1 charges in a non-linear fashion.

Components for Project 11 – 4–60 Second Timer (Fig. 30)

Resistors: all 1/3 watt 5%

R1   33 k (orange, orange, orange, gold)
R2   33 k (orange, orange, orange, gold)
R3   1 k (brown, black, red, gold)
R4   1 M (brown, black, green, gold)
R5   1 M (brown, black, green, gold)
VR1   100 k lin. carbon

Capacitors.

C1   33 μF 10 V tantalum bead

Semiconductors:

IC1   TLO81CP
D1   TIL209 (0.125 in red LED)

Switches:

S1   Push-to-make, release-to-break type
S2   SPST miniature toggle type

Battery:

B1   PP6 size 9 volt and connector to suit

Miscellaneous:

Verobloc
Control knob
Wire

Project 12 — Audio-Alarm Timer

The majority of this circuit is the same as that of the 4 to 60 Second Timer just described. However, it has some additional circuitry which produces an audio tone at the end of the timing period in addition to the LED indicator switching on. This feature is often advantageous as it removes the need to keep an eye on the unit so that the user does not miss the instant when the LED indicator switches on. The timing range of the unit is the same as that of the original circuit, but as we shall see later on, it is very easy to modify the timing range if desired.

Refer to Figure 32 for the complete circuit diagram of the Audio-Alarm Timer, and to Figure 33 for the component layout of the circuit on the Verobloc.

The timer circuit proper is just the same as the original timer in every respect, and the only new circuitry is that associated with IC2 and D2. IC2 is used as a simple audio oscillator of a type that has been employed in earlier circuits. However, when IC1's output is high a bias current is fed from the output of IC1 to the input of IC2 via R6 and D2. This biases IC2 so that its output is fully positive and the circuit is not able to oscillate.

When the output of IC1 goes low at the end of the timing period only a very low voltage appears at the junction of R6 and R7, and this is insufficient to overcome the forward threshold voltage of D1. The bias current through D1 is therefore cut off and the oscillator functions normally, producing the audio alarm tone.

Both timer circuits have a reset switch (S1) incidentally, and in order to start a new timing run this switch is briefly operated. This simply discharges C2 so that the circuit starts a fresh timing-run with C2 at zero charge when S1 is released. Note that the timing-run commences when S1 is released, and not when it is depressed.

The timing range of the unit can be altered by changing the value of the component used in the R3 position. Raising the value of this component produces a proportionate increase in all the delay times, and reducing its value gives a proportionate decrease in these times. For example, using a 10 Megohm resistor for R3 would increase the timing range limits by a factor of 10, and the approximate maximum and minimum figures would be 40 seconds to 600 seconds (10 minutes). Note that 10 Megohms is about the maximum practical value for R3 since with higher values the leakage current of C2 could cause problems. In theory no current leaks through the insulation of C2, but in any practical component there is a small leakage current. If R3 is made too high in value the charge current will become little more than the leakage current and the time delays would consequently become greatly extended. It could even result in the timing period not ending in an extreme case due to the charge current only equalling the leakage current. The charge voltage on C2 would then remain static.

C2 needs to be a good quality low-leakage component, and it is for this reason that a tantalum bead capacitor has been specified in preference to an electrolytic type.

Components for Project 12 – Audio-Alarm Timer (Fig. 32)
   Resistors: all 1/3 watt 5%

R1	33 k (orange, orange, orange, gold)
R2	33 k (orange, orange, orange, gold)
R3	1M (brown, black, green, gold)
R4	1 M (brown, black, green, gold)
R5	1 k (brown, black, red, gold)
R6	10 k (brown, black, orange, gold)
R7	1 k (brown, black, red, gold)
R8	4.7 k (yellow, violet, red, gold)
R9	4.7 k (yellow, violet, red, gold)
VR1	100 k lin. carbon

   Capacitors:

C1	100 nF polyester (brown, black, yellow, black, red)
C2	33 μF 10V tantalum
C3	10 nF polyester (brown, black, orange, black, red)
C4	10 μF 25 V electrolytic

   Semiconductors:

IC1	TLO81CP
IC2	LM380N
D1	TIL209 (0.125 in red LED)
D2	1N4148

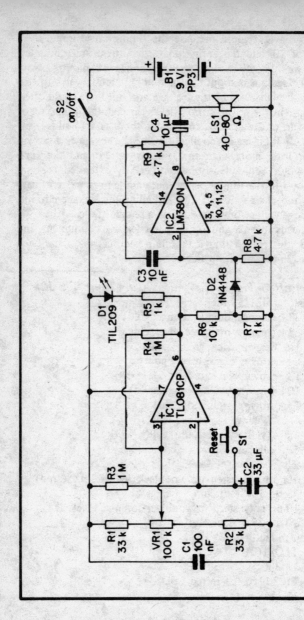

Fig. 32 The circuit diagram of the Audio-Alarm Timer

72

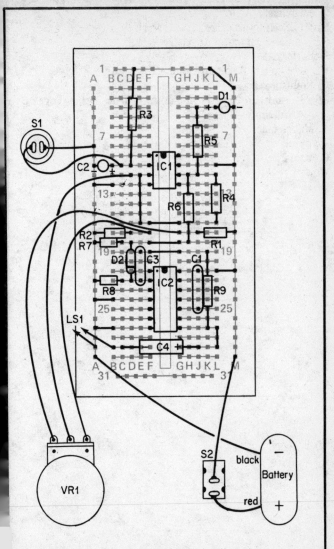

Fig. 33 Constructional details of the Audio-Alarm Timer

Switches:
S1   Push-to-make, release-to-break type
S2   SPST miniature toggle type
Battery:
B1   PP6 size 9 volt and connector to suit
Loudspeaker:
LS1   Miniature type having an impedance in the range 40 to 80 ohms
Miscellaneous:
Verobloc
Control knob
Wire

Project 13 – Simple Oscillator

This simple audio oscillator produces roughly a sinewave output at a frequency of about 500 Hertz. It is suitable for use as a general-purpose audio signal source for use in the home electronics workshop, or if the output is coupled to a crystal earphone and the on/off switch is replaced with a Morse key the unit can be used as a Morse code practice oscillator.

The circuit diagram of the Simple Oscillator can be found in Figure 34, and the Verobloc component layout for this project is illustrated in Figure 35.

The circuit is little more than a basic phase-shift oscillator, and this type of circuit uses positive feedback between the input (base) and output (collector) of a high-gain common emitter-amplifier. However, the base and collector of a common emitter stage are out-of-phase, and any straightforward feedback between the two will be negative rather than positive. This is overcome by using three phase-shift circuits in the feedback path, and each phase-shifter gives a 60 degree phase-shift or 180 degrees through the three circuits, giving positive feedback rather than the negative variety. Provided the gain of the amplifier exceeds the losses through the phase-shift network the circuit will oscillate at the frequency where the phase-shift network gives the 180 degree phase shift.

In this circuit Tr1 is used as a conventional common-emitter stage having R1 as the collector-load resistor and R2 to provide base biasing. C2 plus R4 form the first phase-shift circuit, and C4 plus R3 form the second. The third section is comprised of C3 plus the input impedance of Tr1.

As the gain of Tr1 is somewhat more than the losses through the phase-shift network the circuit does oscillate, but there is not a great excess of gain provided by Tr1, and the circuit does not oscillate very strongly. As a result of this the output waveform is roughly sinewave, although there is a significant harmonic content on the output (harmonics are simply signals at frequencies which are multiples of the fundamental output frequency). This reasonably pure signal makes the unit a good general-purpose test oscillator or Morse practice oscillator.

C1 couples the output signal from the collector of Tr1 to

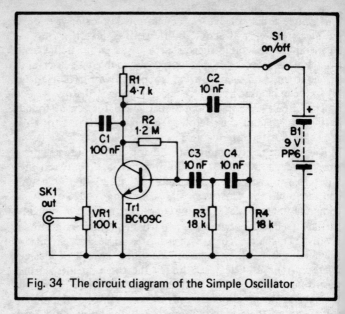

Fig. 34 The circuit diagram of the Simple Oscillator

volume control VR1, and from here the signal is taken to the output socket.

Components for Project 13 – Simple Oscilator (Fig. 34)
　　Resistors: all 1/3 watt 5% (10% over 1 M)
R1　　4.7 k (yellow, violet, red, gold)
R2　　1.2 M (brown, red, green, silver)
R3　　18 k (brown, grey, orange, gold)
R4　　18 k (brown, grey, orange, gold)
VR1　　100 k log. carbon
　　Capacitors:
C1　　100 nF polyester (brown, black, yellow, black, red)
C2　　10 nF polyester (brown, black, orange, black, red)
C3　　10 nF polyester (brown, black, orange, black, red)
C4　　10 nF polyester (brown, black, orange, black, red)
　　Semiconductor:
Tr1　　BC109C

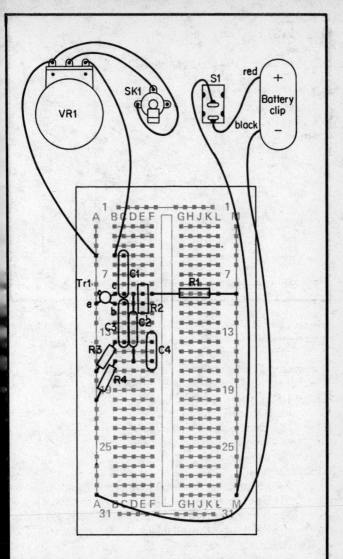

Fig. 35 Constructional details of the Simple Oscillator

Switch:
S1   SPST miniature toggle type
   Battery:
B1   PP6 size 9 volt and connector to suit
   Socket:
SK1   3.5 mm jack type
   Miscellaneous:
Verobloc
Control knob
Wire

Project 14 – Loudspeaker Oscillator

When used as a Morse practice oscillator the circuit of Figure 36 may be preferred to the basic circuit just described, as the circuit of Figure 36 has an additional output stage which enables a loudspeaker to be driven at good volume.

The basic tone-generator circuit is the same as before, but a resistor (R5) has been added at the output of the unit. This is used merely to reduce the output level of the unit which would otherwise be excessive and would fully drive the output stage even with the volume control set well back.

The output stage is a straightforward amplifier based on the LM380N, and this drives a high-impedance loudspeaker (LS1) via DC blocking capacitor C6.

Figure 37 shows the Verobloc component layout for the Loudspeaker Oscillator.

Components for Project 14 – Loudspeaker Oscillator (Fig. 36)
Resistors: all 1/3 watt 5% (10% over 1 M)

R1	18 k (brown, grey, orange, gold)
R2	18 k (brown, grey, orange, gold)
R3	1.2 M (brown, red, green, silver)
R4	4.7 k (yellow, violet, red, gold)
R5	1 M (brown, black, green, gold)
VR1	100 k log. carbon

Capacitors:

C1	100 nF polyester (brown, black, yellow, black, red)
C2	10 nF polyester (brown, black, orange, black, red)
C3	10 nF polyester (brown, black, orange, black, red)
C4	10 nF polyester (brown, black, orange, black, red)
C5	100 nF polyester (brown, black, yellow, black, red)
C6	10 μF 25 V electrolytic

Semiconductors:

IC1	LM380N
Tr1	BC109C

Switch:

S1	SPST miniature toggle type

Battery:

B1	PP6 size 9 volt and connector to suit

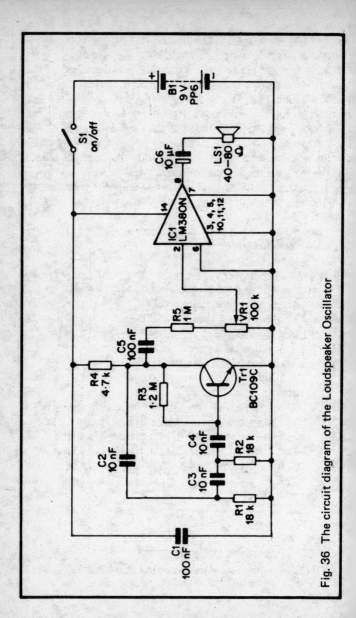

Fig. 36 The circuit diagram of the Loudspeaker Oscillator

80

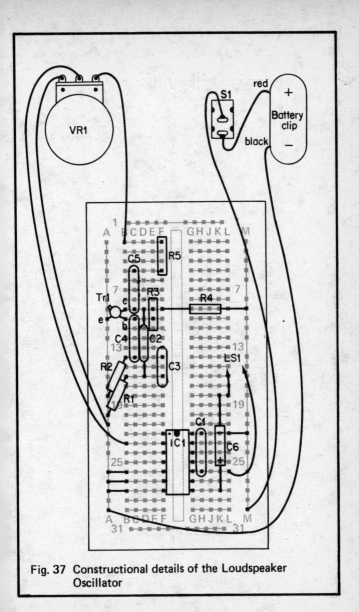

Fig. 37 Constructional details of the Loudspeaker
Oscillator

Loudspeaker:

LS1   Miniature type having an impedance in the range 40 to 80 ohms

Miscellaneous:

Verobloc
Control knob
Wire

Project 15 – Tone Generator

The simple Tone Generator circuit of Figure 38 has sufficient output to drive a high-impedance loudspeaker at good volume, and in a single range it covers a frequency span of about 100 Hertz to 2 kilohertz.

The circuit uses an oscillator of a type which has been employed in prevous projects in this book, and it really just consists of a non-inverting amplifier using an LM380N device with feedback provided from the output to the input via R2, VR1, C3, and R1. As was mentioned in an earlier section of this book, the frequency of oscillation can be altered by changing the values of any of these components, with increased value giving decreased operating frequency, and vice versa.

In this circuit by making the series-feedback resistor (i.e. the combined resistance of R2 and VR1) variable the operating frequency of the unit can be varied. With VR1 at maximum resistance the operating frequency is at its minimum figure of approximately 100 Hertz (a deep tone) and at minimum resistance the operating frequency reaches its maximum figure of very roughly 2 kilohertz.

Figure 39 shows the Verobloc component layout for the Tone Generator. Those who like to experiment might like to try changing the values of the components in the feedback circuit to see what effect this has on the frequency span of the unit.

Components for Project 15 – Tone Generator (Fig. 38)
   Resistors: all 1/3 watt 5%
R1   4.7 k (yellow, violet, red, gold)
R2   4.7 k (yellow, violet, red, gold)
VR1   100 k lin. carbon
   Capacitors:
C1   100 nF polyester (brown, black, yellow, black, red)
C2   100 μF 10 V electrolytic
C3   10 nF polyester (brown, black, orange, black, red)
C4   10 μF 25 V electrolytic
   Semiconductor:
IC1   LM380N

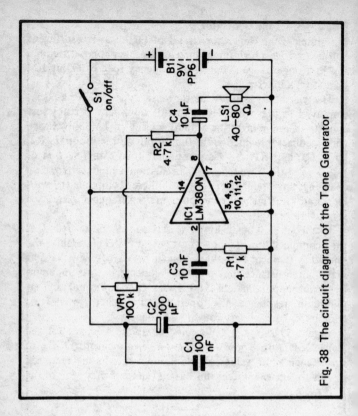

Fig. 38 The circuit diagram of the Tone Generator

Switch:
S1   SPST miniature toggle type
Battery:
B1   PP6 size 9 volt and connector to suit
Loudspeaker:
LS1   Miniature type having an impedance in the range 40 to
      80 ohms
Miscellaneous:
Verobloc
Control knob
Wire

84

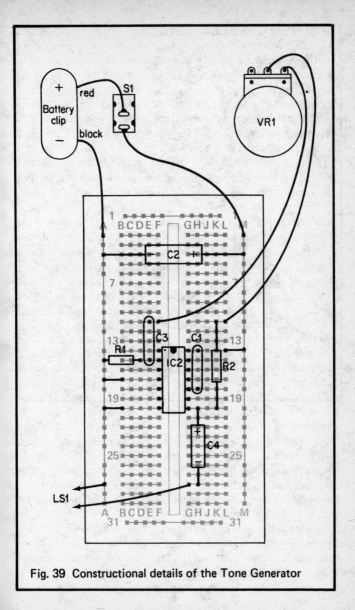

Fig. 39 Constructional details of the Tone Generator

Project 16 – Warbling Doorbuzzer

A simple electronic doorbuzzer could simply consist of an oscillator driving a loudspeaker, but this arrangement is less than ideal in that a simple audio tone tends to be easily masked by other sounds, and it would be ineffective. One way around this problem would be to have a very loud audio tone, but this has the disadvantage of being annoying or even unpleasant to anyone who happens to be close to the loudspeaker when the unit is activated.

A much better, although less obvious alternative, is to use a modulated tone of some kind at only moderate volume. By a modulated tone, we simply mean one that is varied in either frequency or volume. Varying the volume of the signal, perhaps by just pulsing the signal on and off, can be quite effective, but some method of frequency modulation is usually a little more effective. Frequency modulation is usually more pleasing to the ear as well, which is an advantage for something that is for use in the home.

The tone produced by this doorbuzzer circuit is frequency modulated, and the simplest form of frequency modulation is used. The tone is simply switched backwards and forwards between two pitches, and this gives a sort of warbling effect which is quite effective. The full circuit diagram of the unit appears in Figure 40, and the component layout for the breadboard is shown in Figure 41.

The tone-generator circuit is based on IC2 and uses a circuit configuration that has been used in a number of projects described earlier in this book. If Tr1 is switched off, the feedback components which set the frequency of operation are R8, R9, and C4. However, if Tr1 is switched on it effectively shunts R7 across R8, and reduces the value of R8. This increases the operating frequency of the tone generator and the required frequence modulation can thus be obtained by pulsing Tr1 on and off.

This is achieved using a second oscillator based on IC1, and this also uses a type of oscillator which has been used in previous designs in this book, and it will not be described again here. IC1 oscillates at a frequency of a few Hertz, and it switches Tr1 on when its output goes high, and off when its output is low.

You may wish to try experimenting with some of the component values to see if you can obtain an output which you prefer to the one produced using the specified values. Increasing the value of R4 decreases the rate of modulation, while using a lower value increases the modulation frequency. Making R9 higher in value reduces the two tones, and making it lower in value has the opposite effect (the same is true if the value of C4 is changed). Reducing the value of R7 increases the frequency difference between the two tones, and increasing its value has the opposite effect.

Of course, if the unit is constructed as a permanent project S1 would not be a panel mounting push-button switch, but would be a normal bell-push mounted on the door or the door frame (bell-pushes can be obtained from electrical shops, incidentally).

Components for Project 16 – Warbling Doorbuzzer (Fig. 40)
Resistors: all 1/3 watt 5%

R1   33 k (orange, orange, orange, gold)
R2   33 k (orange, orange, orange, gold)
R3   100 k (brown, black, yellow, gold)
R4   1 M (brown, black, green, gold)
R5   18 k (brown, grey, orange, gold)
R6   4.7 k (yellow, violet, red, gold)
R7   18 k (brown, grey, orange, gold)
R8   10 k (brown, black, orange, gold)
R9   10 k (brown, black, orange, gold)
Capacitors:
C1   100 nF polyester (brown, black, yellow, black, red)
C2   100 μF 10 V electrolytic
C3   100 nF polyester (brown, black, yellow, black, red)
C4   10 nF polyester (brown, black, orange, black, red)
C5   10 μF 25 V electrolytic
Semiconductors:
IC1   TLO81CP
IC2   LM380N
Tr1   BC109C

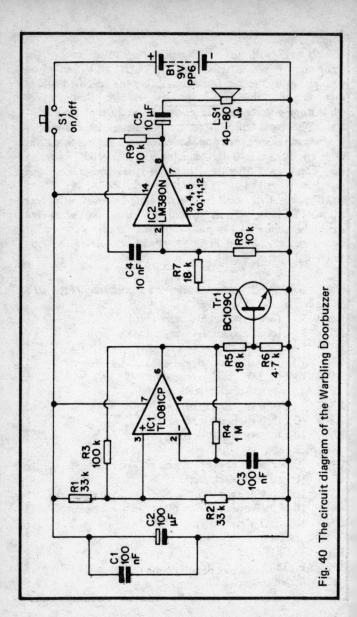

Fig. 40 The circuit diagram of the Warbling Doorbuzzer

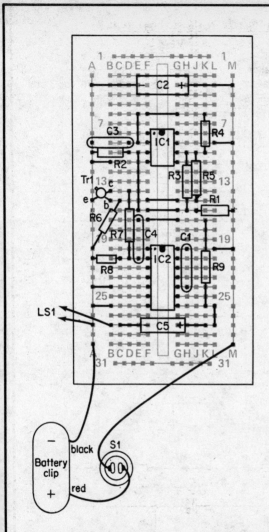

Fig. 41 Constructional details of the Warbling
Doorbuzzer

89

Switch:

S1   Push-to-make, release-to-break type

Battery:

B1   PP6 size 9 volt and connector to suit

Loudspeaker:

LS1   Miniature type having an impedance in the range 40 to 80 ohms

Miscellaneous:

Verobloc

Wire

Project 17 — Two-Tone Train Horn

This is a simple sound effect accessory for a model railway, and it generates a sound which is similar to that produced by the horns used on most modern British Rail locomotives. In other words, it produces an initial fairly low-pitched tone, followed after about half a second or so by a small rise in pitch. This second signal continues until the on/off switch (which is a push-button switch) is released.

Figure 42 shows the complete circuit diagram of the unit and the component layout for the breadboard is given in Figure 43.

IC2 is used as the tone generator, and this device is used in a circuit configuration that has been utilized in several of the previous projects. The rise in pitch is generated by switching on Tr1, which then effectively shunts VR1 across R6. VR1 is adjusted to give a rise in pitch of the correct amount so that a reasonably realistic-sounding output is obtained.

IC1 is used in a simple timing circuit which gives the base bias to Tr1 about half a second or so after switch-on so that the rise in pitch is obtained automatically. R2 and R3 bias the inverting input of IC1 to about half the supply voltage, but zero voltage is applied to the non-inverting input as C1 will be uncharged. However, C1 quickly charges by way of R1 and after roughly half a second the voltage at the non-inverting input exceeds that at the inverting input. IC1's output then goes high and switches on Tr1.

R4 and R5 are used to ensure that the voltage fed to the base of Tr1 when IC1's output is low is not high enough to bias Tr1 into conduction. D1 quickly discharges C1 into the supply lines at switch-off so that the circuit is immediately ready to operate properly again, and the unit will function properly if S1 is operated several times in quick succession.

VR1 is given the correct setting using trial and error to gradually tune the higher tone to the correct pitch. If the unit is constructed as a permanent project VR1 could be made a preset component rather than a panel-mounted control as once it has been given the correct setting it should require no further adjustment.

91

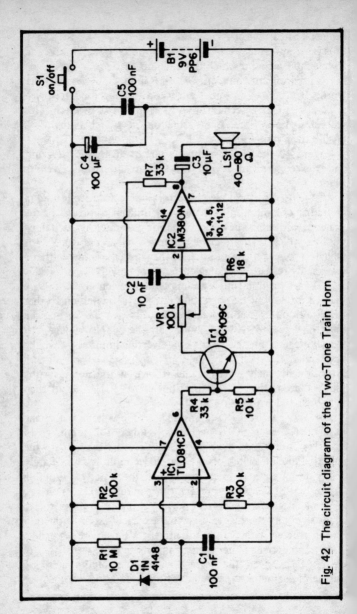

Fig. 42 The circuit diagram of the Two-Tone Train Horn

92

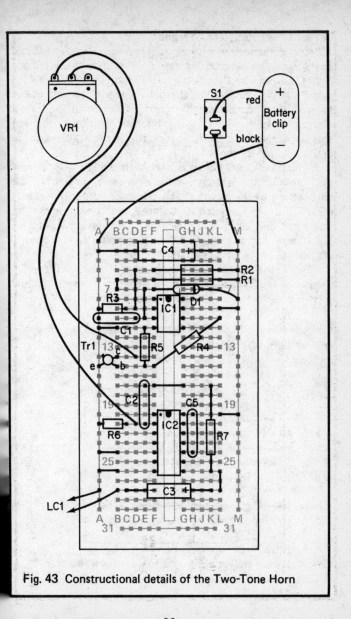

Fig. 43 Constructional details of the Two-Tone Horn

Project 18 – Falling-Tone Version

A train horn does not necessarily produce a higher pitched second tone, and sometimes the higher pitch is the initial one and is followed by the lower tone. The circuit of Figure 42 is easily modified to give this alternative mode of operation, and the modified section of the circuit is shown in the circuit diagram of Figure 44. It is only the timer section of the unit that is changed, and the tone generator is exactly the same as in the original design.

In fact the timer circuit is not substantially different, and the modification merely consists of swopping over the connections to the inputs of IC1. Thus the output is normally high and the higher pitch is produced, and the output swings low when the charge on C1 takes the inverting input to a higher potential than the non-inverting input. Tr1 is then cut off and the lower pitch is produced.

The Verobloc component layout for the falling pitch version of the Two-Tone Train Horn appears in Figure 45, and this only shows the modified section of the layout.

Components for Projects 17 & 18 – Two-Tone Train Horn (Either Version) (Figs. 42 and 44)

Resistors: all 1/3 watt 5% (10% over 1 M)

R1   10 M (brown, black, blue, silver)
R2   100 k (brown, black, yellow, gold)
R3   100 k (brown, black, yellow, gold)
R4   33 k (orange, orange, orange, gold)
R5   10 k (brown, black, orange, gold)
R6   18 k (brown, grey, orange, gold)
R7   33 k (orange, orange, orange, gold)
VR1   100 k lin. carbon

Capacitors:

C1   100 nF polyester (brown, black, yellow, black, red)
C2   10 nF polyester (brown, black, orange, black, red)
C3   10 μF 25 V electrolytic
C4   100 μF 10 V electrolytic
C5   100 nF polyester (brown, black, yellow, black, red)

Semiconductors:

IC1   TLO81CP

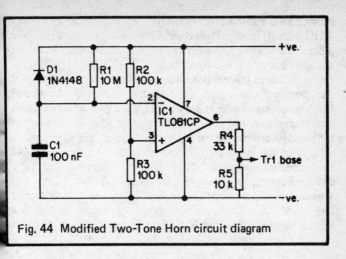

Fig. 44 Modified Two-Tone Horn circuit diagram

Fig. 45 The modified component layout for the
alternative version of the Two-Tone Horn

95

IC2   LM380N
Tr1   BC109C
D1   1N4148
  Switch:
S1   Push-to-make, release-to-break type
  Battery:
B1   PP6 size 9 volt and connector to suit
  Loudspeaker:
LS1   Miniature type having an impedance in the range 40 to
      80 ohms
  Miscellaneous:
Verobloc
Control knob
Wire

Project 19 – Simple Touch-Switch

The advantage of a touch-activated switch over a mechanical switch is simply that there are no moving parts in a touch-activated type. This means that a touch-switch does not wear out, and it should have an operating life equal to the rest of the equipment. Another attraction of this type of switch is simply its novelty value.

This very simple design is of the type where touching two contacts results in some item of equipment being switched on, and the equipment is switched off again when the operator's finger is removed from the contacts. There are two main ways of obtaining a switching action from touch contacts, and one of these is to use stray RF and AF signals picked up in the operator's body to activate the switching circuitry. The other is to use the skin resistance across two contacts to activate the switching circuitry. The second method is probably the more reliable of the two, especially where battery operated equipment is controlled by the touch-switch and it is not possible to rely on a strong "mains hum" signal to activate the circuit. It is therefore this method that has been adopted here.

The circuit diagram of the Simple Touch Switch is given in Figure 46, and the Verobloc component layout appears in Figure 47.

As the circuit stands, Tr1 will not receive any base bias current and is therefore cut off. Tr2 is also cut off as it does not receive any base bias via Tr1. Thus no significant current is applied to the load, which in this case is a relay and LED indicator D2 plus its series current-limiting resistor R3.

If someone touches the two touch contacts a skin resistance of between a few hundred kilohms and a few megohms will be present across the two contacts. This gives only a modest base current to Tr1 of typically only about 10 μA, but this current is amplified and then fed into the base of Tr2. The amplified current is sufficient to bias Tr2 into saturation and the load receives virtually the full supply voltage (there is a small voltage drop of about half a volt across Tr2 but this is too small to be of real significance). If the operator's finger is removed from the touch contacts the base current to Tr1 will be removed, and so will that to Tr2, so that Tr2 switches off and power is removed from the load again. R1 and R2 are current-limiting resistors which are needed to protect the base circuits of Tr1 and Tr2 if a short circuit should be placed across the two touch contacts.

The unit is used to operate a relay and a LED indicator simply as these are convenient ways of showing that the switching action is taking place. The unit can be used to control any piece of 9-volt battery-operated equipment which has a maximum current consumption of no more than 100 mA (which is the maximum current that the BC179 device can handle safely). Make sure that the load is connected with the right polarity. The positive supply is taken from the collector of Tr2 and the negative supply is taken from the negative supply rail of the touch switch circuitry.

The touch contacts can be a couple of fairly large (e.g. M4 size) panel-head screws, or proper touch contacts can be obtained from some of the larger component retailers and would obviously give a very neat and professional finish to the unit. When the circuit is tested on the Verobloc breadboard a

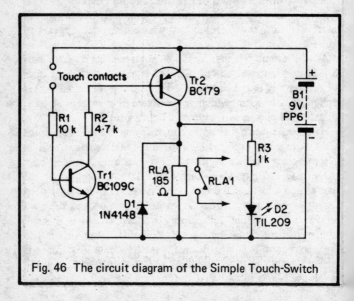

Fig. 46 The circuit diagram of the Simple Touch-Switch

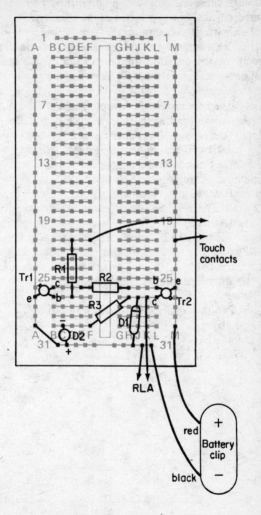

Fig. 47 Constructional details of the Simple Touch-
Switch

couple of bare wires should suffice as the touch contacts, although these will not give good sensitivity unless thick wire is used due to low surface area of the contacts.

The current consumption of the unit in the off state is negligible since only minute leakage currents flow in the circuit. In the on state the current consumption is equal to that of the load plus about 2 mA or so.

Components for Project 19 – Simple Touch-Switch (Fig. 46)
   Resistors: all 1/3 watt 5%
R1   10 k (brown, black, orange, gold)
R2   4.7 k (yellow, violet, red, gold)
R3   1 k (brown, black, red, gold)
   Semiconductors:
Tr1   BC109C
Tr2   BC179
D1   1N4148
D2   TIL209 (0.125 in red LED)
   Relay:
RLA   6/12 volt coil having a resistance of 185 ohms or more,
        and contacts as required (see text)
   Battery:
B1   PP6 size 9 volt and connector to suit
   Miscellaneous:
Verobloc
Touch contacts (see text)
Wire

Project 20 – Touch-Switch

The touch switch described in the previous section of this book is unsuitable for use in many applications because it does not latch in the on state, and in order to keep the controlled equipment switched on it is necessary to continuously touch the two contacts. This can be overcome by using a circuit that does latch in the on state, and also has some means of resetting the circuit to the off state.

This simple circuit has these features, and the load is controlled via two pairs of touch contacts. Touching one set of contacts switches the load on, and the other set of contacts are operated in order to switch the load off again. The circuit diagram of the Touch-Switch is shown in Figure 48, and the Verobloc component layout appears in Figure 49.

The circuit used to switch on the load is basically the same as that employed in the Simple Touch-Switch project described earlier. However, R5 is an additional resistor which keeps Tr2 switched on when the operator's finger is removed from the two "on" touch contacts. This gives the circuit the required latching action.

Operating the two "off" touch contacts results in Tr1 being switched on by the small base-current it receives. This reduces the base-voltage of Tr2 to an insufficient level to keep this component in conduction, and both Tr2 and Tr3 switch off. When the operator's finger is removed from the two "off" contacts the circuit remains in this state since the collector of Tr3 will be at zero volts, and R5 will not provide Tr2 with a base-current. Thus, once again, the required latching action is required.

The notes on constructing and using the Simple Touch-Switch also apply to this design and will not be repeated here.

Components for Project 20 – Touch-Switch (Fig. 48)
    Resistors: all 1/3 watt 5%

R1	10 k (brown, black, orange, gold)
R2	4.7 k (yellow, violet, red, gold)
R3	10 k (brown, black, orange, gold)
R4	4.7 k (yellow, violet, red, gold)
R5	1 M (brown, black, green, gold)

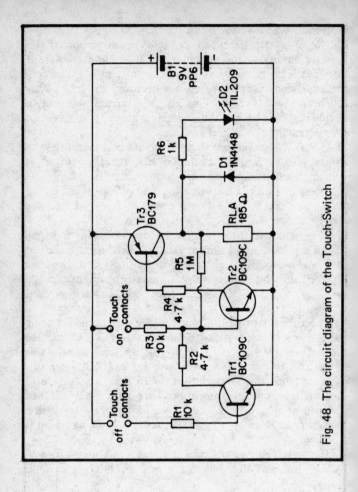

Fig. 48 The circuit diagram of the Touch-Switch

R6   1 k (brown, black, red gold)
   Semiconductors:
Tr1   BC109C
Tr2   BC109C
Tr3   BC179
D1   1N4148
D2   TIL209 (0.125 in red LED)

102

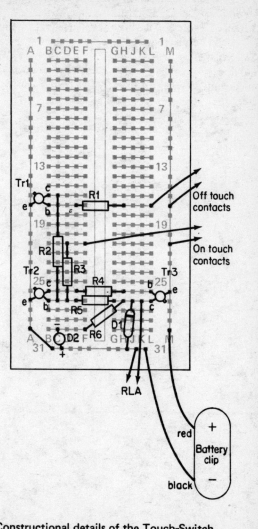

Fig. 49 Constructional details of the Touch-Switch

Battery:
B1   PP6 size 9 volt and connector to suit
    Relay:
RLA   6/12 volt coil having a resistance of 185 ohms or more,
        contacts as required (see text)
    Miscellaneous:
Verobloc
Touch contacts (see text)
Wire

Project 21 — Transistor Checker

Some means of testing transistors is virtually a necessity for the home electronics workshop, and for most purposes it is not necessary to have a highly complex and expensive transistor analyser. All that is really needed is a simple and inexpensive device that will give "go/no—go" checks on the majority of transistor types. This project is suitable for quick checks on silicon transistors (the type normally employed in modern designs), and can be used with PNP and NPN types. It is not really suitable for use with germanium devices, although these are nearly all obsolete and are very uncommon these days. It is not suitable for use with special types of transistor such as FET and unijunction types, but this is a failing of many transistor-tester designs, including some quite sophisticated and expensive ones.

In order to test a device it is simply plugged into the unit, and separate sockets are provided for PNP and NPN devices. If the device is functioning properly a LED indicator will pulse on and off at roughly 2 Hertz (i.e. two flashes per second). Separate LED indicators are used for NPN and PNP devices.

Refer to Figure 50 for the circuit diagram of the Transistor Checker, and Figure 51 for details of the Verobloc component layout and other wiring.

The circuit is basically just an oscillator using a LM380N device in a configuration which has been utilized in several earlier projects. However, the timing component values (R1, C2, and R2) are much larger in this circuit so that the circuit operates at a sub-audio frequency of just a couple of Hertz. There is sufficient feedback to produce strong oscillation and the output waveform is virtually a squarewave.

If we consider the unit in the NPN mode first, with a test device (TrN) connected in circuit this device will be cut off when IC1's output goes low, and biased hard into conduction when IC1's output goes high. The collector load for the test device is LED indicator D1 and its current limiting resistor R5. D1 therefore lights up each time IC1's output goes high, and D1 therefore flashes on and off to indicate that the test transistor is serviceable.

If the test device should happen to have a short circuit

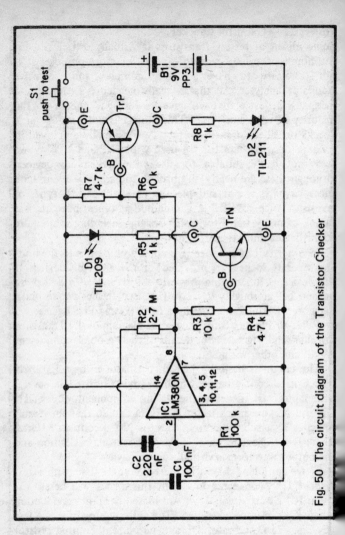

Fig. 50 The circuit diagram of the Transistor Checker

between the base and collector terminals this will result in a forward bias being applied to D1 each time IC1's output goes low, but the bias current will be too low to operate D1 properly and it will be obvious that the test device is faulty. If

106

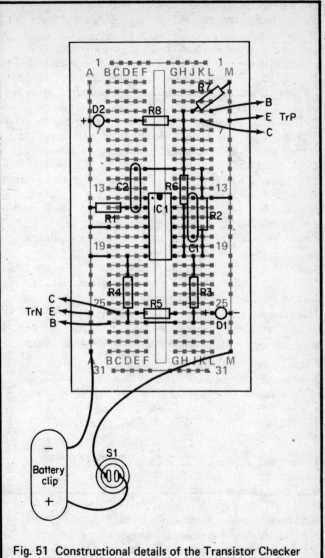

Fig. 51 Constructional details of the Transistor Checker

the test device is closed circuit D1 will simply glow continuously, and it will fail to light at all if the test transistor is open circuit.

The circuit works in much the same way in the PNP mode except that the base terminal is fed from the output of IC1 via R6 and R7, D2 and R8 are the LED indicator and current limiting resistor, and the test device is pulsed on when IC1's output is low rather than when it is high.

Most transistors will plug into the Verobloc without any difficulty and there is no difficulty in using the breadboarded version of the unit. When initially testing the unit a BC109C can be used for TrN and a BC179 can be used for TrP. If the unit is constructed as a permanent project the test devices must be connected to the unit via two sets of three sockets fitted on the front panel of the unit and 1 mm wander sockets are suitable. If these are closely grouped in sets of three it should be found that most devices can be plugged directly into them. A set of test leads terminated in crocodile clips can be used to make the connections to devices that will not plug directly into the sockets. Use wire of a different colour for each lead so that they are easily identified and there is little risk of inadvertently connecting the test device incorrectly.

The table given below should help the user to correctly interpret the results obtained when using the unit.

— LED indicator flashes from fully off to fully on; test device fully serviceable.
— LED flashes dimly; short circuit between collector and base.
— LED lights continuously; collector — emitter short circuit.
— LED fails to light; collector—emitter open circuit.

Components for Project 21 — Transistor Checker (Fig. 50)
  Resistors: all 1/3 watt 5% (10% over 1 M)
R1   100 k (brown, black, yellow, gold)
R2   2.7 M (red, violet, green, silver)
R3   10 k (brown, black, orange, gold)
R4   4.7 k (yellow, violet, red, gold)
R5   1 k (brown, black, red, gold)
R6   10 k (brown, black, orange, gold)

R7 .4.7 k (yellow, violet, red, gold)
R8 1 k (brown, black, red, gold)
   Capacitors:
C1 100 nF polyester (brown, black, yellow, black, red)
C2 220 nF polyester (red, red, yellow, black, red)
   Semiconductors:
IC1 LM380N
D1 TIL209 (0.125 in red LED)
D2 TIL211 (0.125 in green LED)
   Switch:
S1 Push-to-make, release-to-break type
   Battery:
B1 PP6 size 9 volt and connector to suit
   Miscellaneous:
Verobloc
Wire

Project 22 – Reaction Game

On the face of it this is a very simple reaction-testing game whch should not prove at all difficult to complete, but it is actually a little more difficult than may at first appear. The unit has a LED indicator which flashes on and off at typically a little under 1 Hertz (i.e. a little less than once per second), and the idea of the game is simply to hold down a push button switch during the periods when the indicator light is switched off. This charges up a capacitor, and when the charge has reached a sufficiently high level there is a second LED which switches on to indicate that the game has been successfully completed.

While it might seem that all one has to do is to continuously hold the switch down, this is not in fact correct and will not result in the completion of the game. The reason for this is simply that during the periods when the flashing LED is switched on, if the push button switch is operated the charge on the capacitor is almost instantly removed. Thus, in order to complete the game it is necessary to make sure that the push button switch is never operated while the flashing LED is switched on. Remember, even if the required charge has nearly been reached, momentarily operating the switch at the wrong time takes you virtually right back to the beginning again.

The circuit diagram of the Reaction Game can be found in Figure 52, and the Verobloc component layout is illustrated in Figure 53.

IC1 is used in a simple oscillator circuit operating at a low frequency and driving LED indicator D1 which is flashed on during negative output half-cycles from IC1. The inverting input of IC2 is fed from charge storage capacitor C3 while the non-inverting input is biased to about 75% of the supply voltage by R4 and R5. Initially C3 will carry no charge and will supply zero volts to the inverting input of IC2, and IC2's output therefore goes high. LED indicator D2 is switched off at this stage.

If S1 is closed while IC1's output is high (and D1 is switched off) C3 will charge from the output of IC1 via R3. If S1 is operated at the correct times the charge on C3 gradually builds up until the voltage fed to IC2's inverting

110

input is greater than the bias voltage fed to the non-inverting input. The output of IC2 then goes low and D2 switches on to indicate that the game has been successfully completed.

If S1 should be closed while IC1's output is low (and D1 is switched on) the charge on C3 will almost instantly be lost through D3 and the output circuitry of IC1.

Components for Project 22 – Reaction Game (Fig. 52)
  Resistors. all 1/3 watt 5%
R1   1 M (brown, black, green, gold)
R2   1 k (brown, black, red, gold)
R3   100.k (brown, black, yellow, gold)
R4   33 k (orange, orange, orange, gold)
R5   100 k (brown, black, yellow, gold)
R6   1 k (brown, black, red, gold)
  Capacitors:
C1   100 nF polyester (brown, black, yellow, black, red)
C2   220 nF polyester (red, red, yellow, black, red)
C3   33 μF 10 V tantalum bead
  Semiconductors:
IC1   LM380N
IC2   TLO81CP
D1   TIL209 (0.125 in red LED)
D2   TIL211 (0.125 in green LED)
D3   1N4148
  Switches:
S1   Push-to-make, release-to-break type
S2   SPST miniature toggle type
  Battery:
B1   PP6 size 9 volt and connector to suit
  Miscellaneous:
Verobloc
Wire

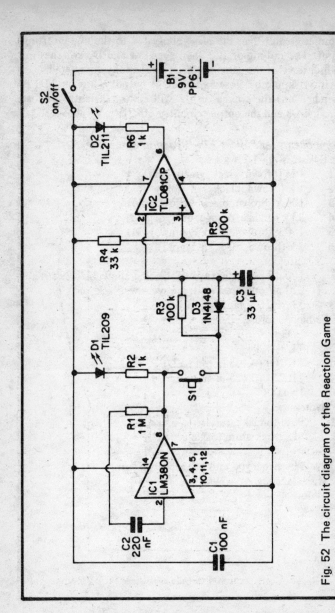

Fig. 52 The circuit diagram of the Reaction Game

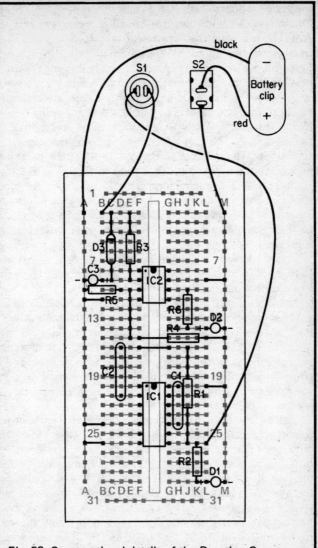

Fig. 53 Constructional details of the Reaction Game

Project 23 – Sound-Activated Switch

The most common uses for sound-activated switches are probably the automatic control of tape recorders and radio transceivers, but no doubt there are numerous other applications for this type of equipment. The simple design featured here can be activated by speech at normal volume at a range of up to about 1 metre or so, and this is adequate for most practical applications. Higher sensitivity is not really a good idea as it is merely likely to lead to spurious operation of the device, and has no real advantages under normal operating conditions. The microphone used in the unit is a high impedance loudspeaker which is used in reverse as a sort of crude moving coil microphone. This does not give very good sound quality, but as the microphone is only used to produce a signal which is amplified and used to control a relay (which in turn operates the controlled equipment) this is of no consequence.

Figure 54 shows the circuit diagram of the Sound-Activated Switch and the component layout of the breadboard and other wiring of the unit are illustrated in Figure 55.

IC1 is used as a straightforward inverting amplifier having a voltage gain of approximately 80 dB (10,000 times), although the gain is substantially less than this at higher audio frequencies since IC1 simply is not able to give such a high voltage gain at these frequencies. It is necessary to use this large amount of amplification due to the very low signal voltage provided by the microphone, which will normally be less than a millivolt.

The output from IC1 is coupled by C3 to a rectifier and smoothing circuit which consists of D1, D2, C4, and R5. This produces a positive DC bias which is fed to the inverting input of IC2. This circuit produces a DC signal that has a fast attack time so that the unit quickly responds to the commencement of an input signal and almost instantly switches on the controlled equipment. However, the decay time is much slower, and this is advantageous since it prevents the controlled equipment from being switched off during brief pauses of the type that occur in normal speech.

IC2 is used as the relay driver, and R6 provides a small

positive bias to the non-inverting input of this device. This keeps the output in the high state and the relay switched off until a suitably strong input signal produces a strong enough bias at the inverting input of IC2 to send the output low and thus switch on the relay.

The unit is capable of controlling practically any item of electronic or electrical equipment, but make sure that the relay you use has contacts that are up to the task and are not being overloaded. In its breadboarded form the unit cannot control a piece of mains-operated equipment as this would leave dangerous mains wiring exposed. It can be used to control mains operated equipment if it is constructed as a permanent project and the necessary safety precautions are observed. However, it would be inadvisable for inexperienced constructors to use the unit to control mains powered equipment.

Components for Project 23
– Sound-Activated Switch (Fig. 54)
    Resistors: all 1/3 watt 5% (10% over 1 M)
R1   1 k (brown, black, red, gold)
R2   100 k (brown, black, yellow, gold)
R3   100 k (brown, black, yellow, gold)
R4   10 M (brown, black, blue, silver)
R5   100 k (brown, black, yellow, gold)
R6   1 M (brown, black, green, gold)
    Capacitors:
C1   1 μF 63 V electrolytic
C2   2.2 μF 63 V electrolytic
C3   4.7 μF 63 V electrolytic
C4   10 μF 25 V electrolytic
C5   100 nF polyester (brown, black, yellow, black, red)
C6   100 μF 10 V electrolytic
    Semiconductors:
IC1   TLO81CP
IC2   LM380N
D1   OA90
D2   0A90
D3   1N4148

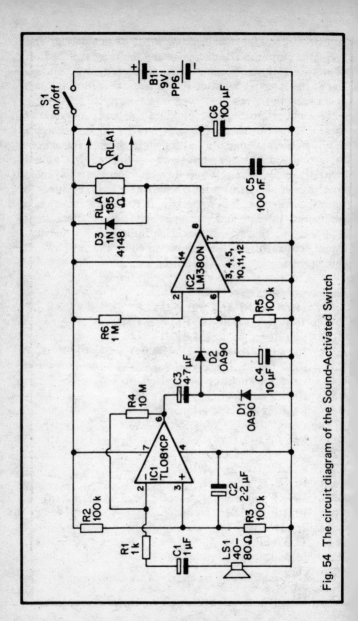

Fig. 54 The circuit diagram of the Sound-Activated Switch

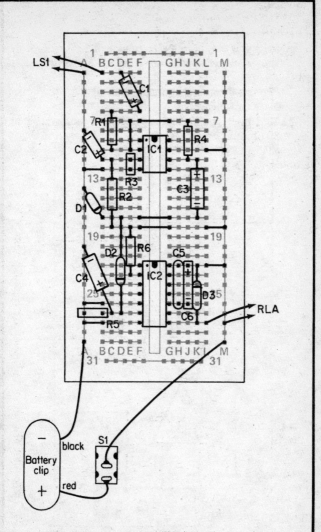

Fig. 55 Constructional details of the Sound-Activated
Switch

117

Switch:

S1   SPST miniature toggle type

Relay:

RLA   6/12 volt coil having a resistance of 185 ohms or more and contacts of adequate rating and correct type

Battery:

B1   PP6 size 9 volt and connector to suit

Loudspeaker (microphone):

LS1   Miniature type having an impedance in the range 40 to 80 ohms

Miscellaneous:

Verobloc

Wire

Project 24 – Slide Timer

This project can be used with a projector having a remote control socket to provide automatic slide changing with an interval between slide changes that is continuously variable between approximately 6 and 25 seconds. The unit controls the projector via a relay, and it is merely necessary for the relay to be briefly pulsed on at the appropriate frequency. It is not necessary for the relay to be switched on for the exact length of time a slide change takes since the automatic slide change mechanism of projectors have a built-in latching action. It is merely necessary for the relay to be closed long enough to latch this mechanism.

Refer to Figure 56 for the circuit diagram of the Slide Change Timer, and to Figure 57 for the Verobloc component layout and wiring of the unit.

The oscillator is based on IC1 and uses the same configuration as that employed in the Metronome project which was described earlier in this publication. The frequency of operation is much lower in this case though, and is set using VR1 to give slide changes at the required spacing. The relay is driven from the output of IC1 via emitter-follower buffer Tr1 which gives the current amplification needed in order to drive the relay properly. RLA1 is a normally open relay contact which is used to activate the projector each time the relay is pulsed on.

SK1 is connected to the appropriate socket on the projector using a twin lead which does not need to be a screened type. It is fitted with a 3.5 mm plug which connects to SK1, and a plug of the appropriate type for the socket on the projector.

A 4-pole miniature relay was used for RLA1 in the prototype Slide Timer unit, and Figure 57 shows a relay having this type of base. Obviously the wiring to the relay base must be modified slightly if another type of relay is used, and the retailer's data should give details of the relay's base connections. With a little experimentation and common sense it should be possible to find the correct method of connection even if base connection data is not available.

119

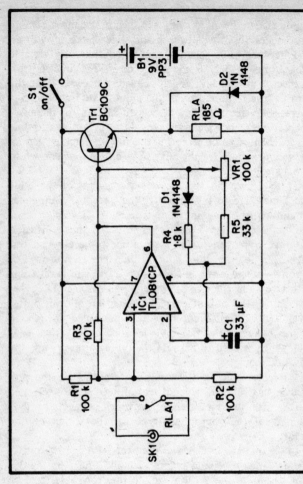

Fig. 56 The circuit diagram of the Slide Timer

Components for Project 24 – Slide Timer (Fig. 56)
    Resistors: all 1/3 watt 5%

R1   100 k (brown, black, yellow, gold)
R2   100 k (brown, black, yellow, gold)
R3   10 k (brown, black, orange, gold)
R4   1.8 k (brown, grey, red, gold)

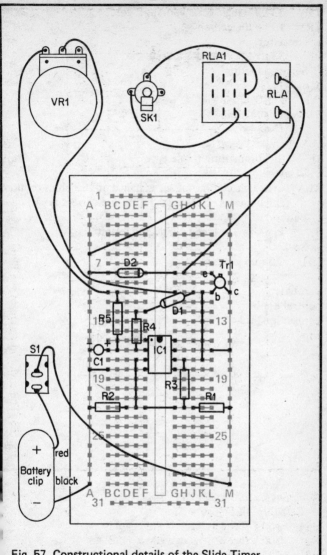

Fig. 57 Constructional details of the Slide Timer

R5   33 k (orange, orange, orange, gold)
VR1   100 k lin. carbon
  Capacitor:
C1   33 μF 10 V tantalum bead
  Semiconductors:
IC1   TLO81CP
Tr1   BC109C
D1   1N4148
D2   1N4148
  Switch:
S1   SPST miniature toggle type
  Relay:
RLA 6/12 volt coil having a resistance of 185 ohms or more
       and contacts of adequate rating and correct type
  Battery:
B1   PP6 size 9 volt and connector to suit
  Socket:
SK1   3.5 mm jack socket
  Miscellaneous:
Verobloc
Control knob
Connection lead
Wire

Project 25 — Moisture Detector

This circuit normally produces a low frequency audio output having a fundamental frequency of only a few Hertz, but the operating frequency rises considerably if a couple of probes are placed in water. A more modest increase in pitch is produced if the probes are placed in something damp, such as fairly moist soil. In other words the unit acts as a simple form of moisture detector with the rise in pitch corresponding to the degree of moisture detected. A practical application for a unit such as this is as a soil moisture indicator to show whether or not a plant needs watering by giving an indication of the moisture at root level.

The circuit diagram of the unit is shown in Figure 58 and the Verobloc component layout is given in Figure 59.

The circuit is little more than a low frequency oscillator based on IC1 and driving loudspeaker LS1 via C2. The frequency at which IC1 oscillates can be considerably boosted by switching on Tr1 so that R3 is effectively connected from the input of IC1 to the negative supply rail. As the circuit stands though, Tr1 is cut off and passes no significant current.

With the probes placed in water there will be a fairly low resistance between them, and a heavy base current will flow into Tr1 so that this device is biased hard into conduction and the frequency of IC1 is taken to its maximum figure. It should perhaps be pointed out that pure water does in fact have a very high resistance, but most sources of water (rain, tap water, etc.) contain significant amounts of impurities which produce a much lower resistance.

If the probes are placed in something that has only a modest moisture content there will be a much higher resistance between them, but Tr1 will still be biased into conduction to a certain extent and there will be a significant increase in the operating frequency of the unit. Thus Tr1 is not simply switched fully on or fully off, and intermediate states (and output frequencies from the unit) can be produced. The probes can simply consist of two pieces of single strand PVC-insulated wire with a small length of insulation (say about 5 mm) removed from the ends. If the unit is to be used as a soil moisture indicator the two probes must be mounted

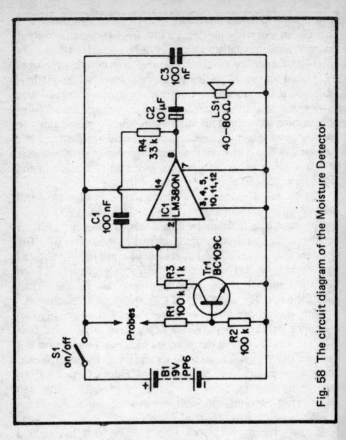

Fig. 58 The circuit diagram of the Moisture Detector

together so that they are a fixed distance apart. A spacing of about 20 mm is suitable. The spacing is important as it effects the sensitivity of the unit. If the unit seems to be oversensitive, incidentally, removing some of the exposed wire at the end of each probe is the easiest way of correcting this. Similarly, a lack of sensitivity can be corrected by removing some of the insulation at the end of each probe to leave a greater length of exposed wire.

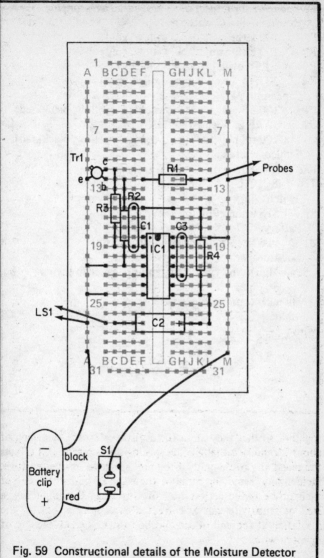

Fig. 59 Constructional details of the Moisture Detector

Components for Project 25 – Moisture Detector (Fig. 58)
    Resistors: all 1/3 watt 5%

R1   100 k (brown, black, yellow, gold)
R2   100 k (brown, black, yellow, gold)
R3   1 k (brown, black, red, gold)
R4   33 k (orange, orange, orange, gold)
    Capacitors:

C1   100 nF polyester (brown, black, yellow, black, red)
C2   10 μF 25 V electrolytic
C3   100 nF polyester (brown, black, yellow, black, red)
    Semiconductors:

IC1   LM380N
Tr1   BC109C
    Switch:

S1   SPST miniature toggle type
    Battery:

B1   PP6 size 9 volt and connector to suit
    Loudspeaker:

LS1   Miniature type having an impedance in the range 40 to
       80 ohms
    Miscellaneous:

Verobloc
Wire

Project 26 — Water Activated Alarm

This device produces an audible warning sound when water is detected by a simple sensor. The audio alarm signal is a tone which is slowly varied up and down in frequency, and this is a very effective form of alarm signal. Possible applications for a unit of this type include use as a rain alarm or cistern overflow alarm.

Refer to Figure 60 for the complete circuit diagram of the Water Activated Alarm, and to Figure 61 for the Verobloc component layout.

The sensor simply consists of two pieces of metal placed very close together and separated by an insulating material. Thus there is normally an extremely high resistance between the two metal electrodes, but if they are bridged by water which has a significant impurity content there will be a fairly low resistance between them. Therefore, Tr2 is normally cut off and passes only minute leakage currents, but if the sensor is activated Tr2 is biased hard into conduction and supplies virtually the full supply voltage to the alarm generator circuit which is based on IC1 and IC2.

IC2 is used as the tone generator and its output is coupled to LS1 by C4. The operating frequency of IC2 can be varied up and down by increasing and decreasing the base current fed to Tr1. This modulation is provided by IC1 which is used as a simple very low frequency oscillator having an operating frequency of only about 0.5 Hertz (i.e. only one cycle every two seconds).

The output of IC1 simply switches straight from the high state to the low one, and back again, producing a squarewave output. This is not suitable as the modulation signal as it would simply switch the tone between the frequencies, rather than giving the smooth variation in pitch which we require here. The signal across C3 is a form of sawtooth waveform which steadily rises as C2 charges, and falls as C2 discharges. It is not actually a linear sawtooth (in other words there is some variation in the rate at which the voltage rises and falls) but this is of no consequence here, and it is this signal that is used to modulate the tone generator. The required loose coupling to the base of Tr1 is provided by R5.

127

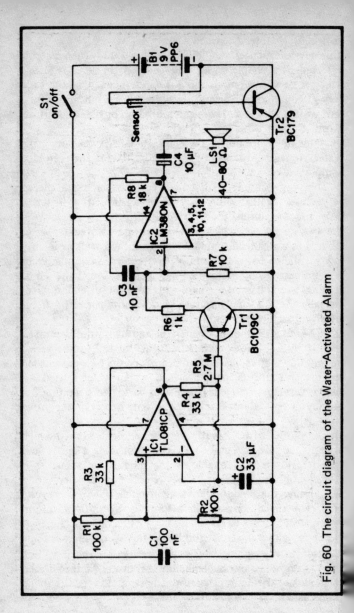

Fig. 60 The circuit diagram of the Water-Activated Alarm

128

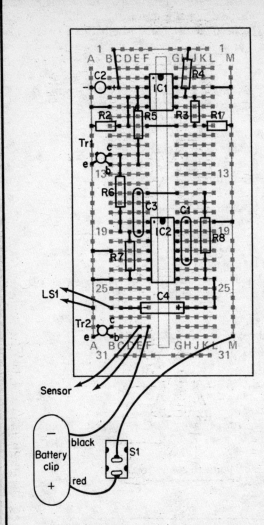

Fig. 61 Constructional details of the Water-Activated
Alarm

129

The sensor can simply consist of two non-insulated wires placed on a plastic or other insulating base, with the smallest possible gap between the two wires. Alternatively a small piece of stripboard or a sensor made from printed circuit board could be used.

Components for Project 26 – Water-Activated Alarm (Fig. 60)
Resistors: all 1/3 watt 5% (10% over 1 M)

R1	100 k (brown, black, yellow, gold)
R2	100 k (brown, black, yellow, gold)
R3	33 k (orange, orange, orange, gold)
R4	33 k (orange, orange, orange, gold)
R5	2.7 M (red, violet, green, silver)
R6	1 k (brown, black, red, gold)
R7	10 k (brown, black, orange, gold)
R8	18 k (brown, grey, orange, gold)

Capacitors:

C1	100 nF polyester (brown, black, yellow, black, red)
C2	33 μF 10 V tantalum
C3	10 nF polyester (brown, black, orange, black, red)
C4	10 μF 25 V electrolytic

Semiconductors:

IC1	TLO81CP
IC2	LM380N
Tr1	BC109C
Tr2	BC179

Switch:

S1	SPST miniature toggle type

Loudspeaker.

LS1	Miniature type having an impedance in the range 40 to 80 ohms

Battery:

B1	PP6 size 9 volt and connector to suit

Miscellaneous:
Verobloc
Sensor (see text)
Wire

Project 27 – Crystal Set

An obvious advantage of a crystal set over any other type of receiver is that it does not require a battery or any other type of power supply. The power to drive the headphones or earphone is derived from the radio signal, but this does give a couple of major disadvantages. One is the need for a fairly large aerial since the output from an ordinary ferrite aerial or a telescopic type is nothing like large enough to operate a crystal receiver. The second disadvantage is that despite the use of a large aerial to give a strong signal a crystal set is still only capable of driving an earphone or headphones, and loudspeaker operation is not really feasible. Nevertheless, a crystal set is an interesting project, and is very simple and inexpensive to build.

Figure 62 shows the circuit diagram of a simple medium-waveband crystal receiver, and the Verobloc component layout for this is given in Figure 63.

L1 is the aerial coil, and VC1 is the tuning capacitor. Together these form a tuned circuit, and this has a very high impedance at or close to the resonant frequency, but a low impedance at other frequencies. By adjusting VC1 to resonate the tuned circuit at the frequency of the desired transmission this signal is able to pass through to the next stage of the circuit, but other transmissions which will be on different frequencies will be effectively short circuited to earth and thus filtered out. L1 is actually a ferrite aerial, but as stated earlier this gives an inadequate output for a crystal set and a more effective aerial is required. This aerial is simply a fairly long length of wire, and its output is coupled directly into the tuned circuit. There is a small coupling winding on L1, but this is not used in this circuit.

The audio signal is modulated onto the RF (radio frequency) carrier wave by varying the strength of the RF signal in sympathy with the amplitude of the audio signal (known as amplitude modulation or AM). It is not possible to simply pass the RF signal through an RF filter to recover the audio modulation since the positive half cycles will cancel out the negative half cycles and give an average output voltage of zero. However, if the RF signal is rectified by a diode and then RF filtering is used, the cancelling effect is avoided and the

131

average signal level is the same as the audio modulation. Thus the required audio signal is obtained using this simple method of demodulation.

In this circuit D1 allows positive half-cycles to pass and blocks negative half-cycles. It does not actually matter which set of half-cycles are used since they are both modulated in exactly the same way, and if the polarity of D1 is reversed the set will still function properly. R1 is needed to provide a discharge path for the RF filter capacitor, and without R1 this capacitor would simply charge up to the peak signal level. R1 ensures that the smoothed output signal rises and falls in sympathy with the average RF signal level so that a proper audio output is obtained. Although the RF filter capacitor may appear to be absent from the circuit, it is in fact provided by the capacitance of the crystal earphone which is fed with the output signal of the receiver, and no extra filter capacitance is required.

When building the receiver, either as a permanent unit or on the Verobloc breadboard, keep the aerial coil reasonably far away (i.e. at least 20 mm or so) from metal objects or the

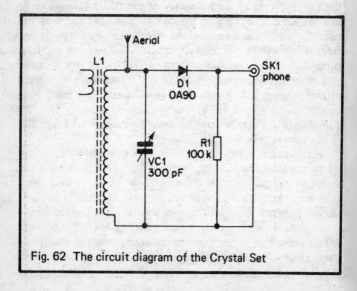

Fig. 62 The circuit diagram of the Crystal Set

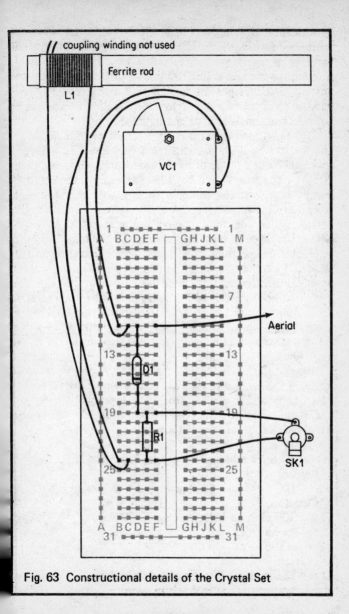

coupling winding not used

Ferrite rod

L1

VC1

1   1
A   B C D E F   G H J K L   M

7

Aerial

13   13

D1

19   19

R1   SK1

25   25

A   B C D E F   G H J K L   M
31   31

Fig. 63 Constructional details of the Crystal Set

performance of the set may suffer. Also, L1 must be positioned at roughly the right place on the ferrite rod or the coverage of the set will not be satisfactory. Finding a suitable position for the coil is simply a matter of trial and error, and any position that permits full coverage of the medium waveband to be obtained is satisfactory. This is almost certain to be with the coil almost right at one end of the rod.

The aerial simply consists of a length of insulated wire, and this can be single or multistrand PVC insulated wire, or a reasonably thick gauge of enamelled copper wire, say about 20 SWG. The wire should be as long as possible, but about 10 metres of wire strung around a room should give reasonable reception of a few stations. A longer outdoor aerial will give better results, and for optimum results about 20 metres of wire set as high as possible and clear of buildings and other large obstructions should be used. The wire should not be allowed to come into electrical contact with buildings, trees, or any other object that could leak some of the signal to earth. Performance can be further improved by using an earth connection, and this can merely consist of a lead attached to a metal pipe which is then buried in the earth about half a metre deep. The lead is then connected to point D–24 on the Verobloc.

Being realistic about it, it is probably not worthwhile spending a great deal of time and money on the installation of a large aerial and an earth system, and it is probably better just to experiment a little and erect the best aerial that can be produced reasonably easily and at low cost.

Components for Project 27 – Crystal Set (Fig. 62)
   Resistor:
R1   100 k 1/3 watt 5% (brown, black, yellow, gold)
   Capacitor:
VC1   300 pF solid dielectric (Jackson Dielecon)
   Semiconductor:
D1   OA90
   Inductor:
L1   Denco MW5FR ferrite aerial or similar

Socket:
SK1   3.5 mm jack socket
    Miscellaneous:
Verobloc
Control knob
Aerial
Wire
Crystal earpiece

Project 28 – Personal MW Radio

This simple receiver gives a level of performance that is similar to that of the crystal set just described, but it uses a ferrite aerial and does not require an external aerial of any kind. In one respect the performance of the set is superior to that of the crystal set, and this is with regard to selectivity. The tuning is not very "sharp" with a crystal set as the aerial and detector both reduce the effectiveness of the tuned circuit due to loading effects. This can result in a second station being heard in the background and spoiling reception of the desired station.

Improved results are obtained with this design since there is no external aerial and consequently no loading effects from this source. The coupling winding on the aerial coil is used to tap off only a relatively small amount of signal from the aerial so that loading is further reduced. A further improvement is obtained by using a technique known as regeneration which also boosts the sensitivity of the receiver.

Figure 64 shows the circuit diagram of the receiver, and the Verobloc component layout is given in Figure 65.

VC1 and the main winding of L1 form the tuned circuit, and the small coupling winding on L1 couples the output of the aerial to the input of a simple common-emitter amplifier which utilizes Tr1 in a conventional configuration. C2 couples the amplified output of Tr1 to a straightforward diode demodulator circuit.

Regeneration is provided by CX which is a very low value capacitor which is actually home contructed from a couple of insulated wires. This merely sends some of the amplified signal at the collector of Tr1 back to the aerial so that it is fed back through Tr1 again for further amplification. This has the obvious effect of boosting the gain of the circuit, but it provides a greater boost in gain at frequencies where the circuit is working efficiently than it does at frequencies where efficiency is poor. In other words, the station to which the receiver is tuned will be received well as the gain of the set will be considerably boosted at this frequency, but stations on other frequencies will receive a relatively low boost and the selectivity of the set is thus improved.

One or two points must be borne in mind when constructing

136

this project. One lead from L1 connects direct to VC1 and not via the breadboard. This connection can either be soldered or a crocodile clip can be used. The lead that carries this connection also forms part of CX, and a single-strand insulated lead from the breadboard forms the other part of CX (see Figure 65). These two leads are twisted together, and up to a point the more they are twisted together the better the performance of the receiver becomes. There is a limit to the boost in performance that can be obtained though, and if this limit is exceeded the circuit will oscillate at some settings of the tuning control. This will be heard as a whistling sound that changes in pitch as the receiver is tuned through a station, and it makes proper reception impossible. Therefore, CX should have the highest capacitance (the two leads twisted together as much as possible) without oscillation occuring at any setting of VC1.

If the receiver is constructed as a permanent project it must be housed in a plastic case, or a case made of some other non-metallic substance. A metal case would shield the ferrite aerial from radio waves and prevent any signals from being received!

If regeneration cannot be obtained, incidentally, this probably means that the phasing of L1 is incorrect and the feedback through CX is negative rather than positive, and is therefore giving a reduction in performance rather than an improvement. To correct this it is merely necessary to swap over the two leads from L1's coupling winding so that the correct phasing is obtained.

Note that the output of this receiver, and the crystal set described earlier, are only suitable for a crystal earphone. A low-impedance magnetic type will not give good results with these designs, and it is unlikely to work at all with them.

Components for Project 28 – Personal MW Radio (Fig. 64)
   Resistors: all 1/3 watt 5% (10% over 1 M)
R1   1.2 M (brown, red, green, silver)
R2   4.7 k (yellow, violet, red, gold)
R3   100 k (brown, black, yellow, gold)
   Capacitors:
C1   100 nF polyester (brown, black, yellow, black, red)

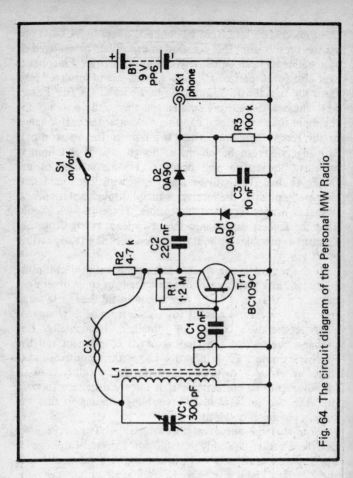

Fig. 64 The circuit diagram of the Personal MW Radio

C2   220 nF polyester (red, red, yellow, black, red)
C3   10 nF polyester (brown, black, orange, black, red)
VC1   300 pF solid dielectric (Jackson Dielecon)
    Semiconductors:
Tr1   BC109C
D1   OA90
D2   OA90

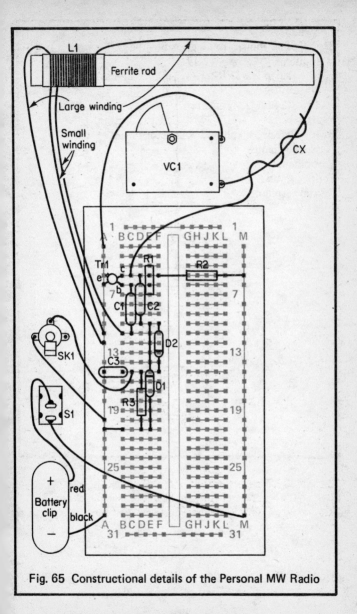

Fig. 65 Constructional details of the Personal MW Radio

Switch:

S1   SPST miniature toggle type

Inductor:

L1   Denco MW5FR ferrite aerial or similar

Socket:

SK1   3.5 mm jack socket

Battery:

B1   PP6 size 9 volt and connector to suit

Miscellaneous:

Verobloc

Control knob

Crystal earphone

Wire

Project 29 – MW Radio

This receiver is simply the one just described but with an audio output stage that enables a loudspeaker to be driven at good volume. The circuit diagram of the receiver is given in Figure 66 and details of the Verobloc component layout are provided in Figure 67.

The circuitry up to the detector stage is exactly the same as the earlier receiver design, and the only difference in the detector circuitry is that volume control VR1 is used in place of the fixed value resistor which was used at this point in the earlier design.

The output stage is a straightforward circuit using the LM380N device. DC blocking capacitor C4 is needed at the input to IC1 because a small DC potential is developed across VR1 when a signal is received, and without C4 this would upset the biasing of IC1. C5 is an additional RF filter capacitor, and this is needed as only a minute RF leakage into IC1 would be sufficient to make the circuit extremely unstable. IC1 drives a high impedance loudspeaker via C6, and reasonable volume should be obtained from the set. Greater volume can be obtained using a lower impedance loudspeaker, but 15 ohms is the lowest recommended speaker impedance for this circuit. In general, the larger the loudspeaker used the greater the volume level that can be produced.

The constructional and setting-up notes for the previous receiver also apply to this one, and in addition, if the unit is constructed as a permanent project, ensure that LS1 and L1 are reasonably well separated. Otherwise stray feedback from the loudspeaker's coil to L1 could cause poor reception or instability.

Components for Project 29 – MW Radio (Fig. 66)
    Resistors: all 1/3 watt 5% (10% over 1 M)

R1   1.2M (brown, red, green, silver)
R2   4.7 k (yellow, violet, red, gold)
VR1   100 k log. carbon
    Capacitors:
C1   100 nF polyester (brown, black, yellow, black, red)
C2   220 nF polyester (red, red, yellow, black, red)

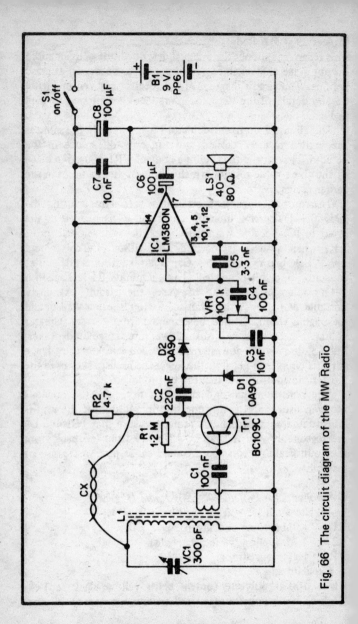

Fig. 66 The circuit diagram of the MW Radio

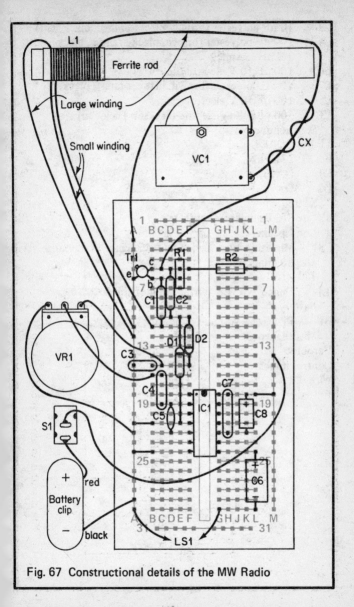

Fig. 67 Constructional details of the MW Radio

143

C3	10 nF polyester (brown, black, orange, black, red)
C4	100 nF polyester (brown, black, yellow, black, red)
C5	3.3 nF ceramic
C6	100 μF 10 V electrolytic
C7	10 nF polyester (brown, black, orange, black, red)
C8	100 μF 10 V electrolytic
VC1	300 pF solid dielectric (Jackson Dielecon)

Semiconductors:

TR1	BC109C
IC1	LM380N
D1	OA90
D2	OA90

Switch:

| S1 | SPST miniature toggle type |

Loudspeaker:

| LS1 | Miniature type having an impedance in the range 40 to 80 ohms (see text) |

Inductor:

| L1 | Denco MW5FR ferrite aerial or similar |

Battery:

| B1 | PP6 size 9 volt and connector to suit |

Miscellaneous:

Verobloc
Control knobs
Wire

Project 30 – Fuzz Unit

This unit is intended for use with an electric guitar and gives the well known and popular "fuzz" effect. This effect is one of the most simple to produce since it merely entails distorting the signal to produce harmonics (multiples of the fundamental frequency). All that is needed in order to achieve this is a simple clipping amplifier such as the one shown in the circuit diagram of Figure 68 (although there are actually other ways of producing the "fuzz" effect).

Basically the circuit is a high gain inverting amplifier using operational amplifier IC1. The gain is set at approximately 40 dB (100 times) by feedback resistors R1, R4, and R5. However, if the output of IC1 swings more than about 0.6 volts positive D2 is biased into conduction and effectively cuts R5 out of circuit. The same thing happens if the output of IC1 goes more than about 0.6 volts negative of its quiescent level, except it is D1 that is biased into conduction and bypasses R5. The result of R5 being bypassed is a reduction in the gain of the circuit to only about unity. The output from an electric guitar will be quite sufficient to drive the output of IC1 to ±0.6 volts, even when the signal has decayed from its initial fairly high amplitude. The signal at the output of the unit is therefore subjected to a sudden drop in gain as the ±0.6 volt threshold level is achieved, giving the required distortion and what is virtually a squarewave output.

C2 is used to provide DC blocking at the output, and VR1 is the output level control. The latter is needed because the output from the Fuzz Unit is considerably stronger than the direct output from many guitar pick-ups, and VR1 enables the output of the Fuzz Unit to be set at about the same level as the direct output of the pick-up used with the unit.

Figure 69 shows the Verobloc component layout for the Fuzz Unit. The input and output of the breadboard can be connected to 6.35 mm (¼ in) jack sockets which in turn connect to the usual screened jack leads that are used to connect items of musical equipment to one another. Alternatively four short crocodile clip leads can be used to connect the breadboard to the two jack leads. Of course, the guitar connects to the input of the unit (SK1) and the output (SK2)

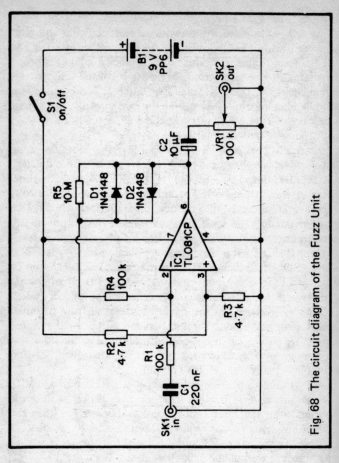

Fig. 68 The circuit diagram of the Fuzz Unit

connects to the input of the guitar amplifier. If there seems to be a very high level of mains hum this probably means that the two leads to SK1 or the two to SK2 are connected around the wrong way. The negative supply rail of the unit (row A) connects to the outer braiding of the input and output leads (the barrels of the jack plugs). The non-earthy input and output leads connect to the inner conductors of the jack leads (the tips of the jack plugs).

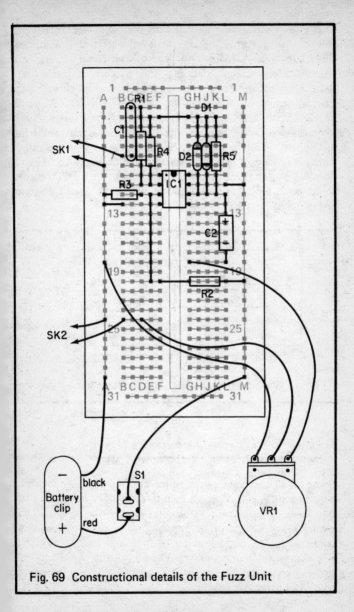

Fig. 69 Constructional details of the Fuzz Unit

If you construct the unit as a permanent project it is advisable to use a strong metal case for the unit, and a diecast aluminium type is ideal. This type of case is very tough and gives excellent screening against stray pick-up of mains hum and other electrical noise. It is normal for a unit of this type to have a bypass switch so that the unit can be switched in and out of circuit very easily. If a heavy duty push-button type switch is used as the bypass switch, and this is fitted on the lid of the unit, it can be operated by foot while playing the guitar which is obviously more convenient than having to use a hand operated type. The bypass switch needs to be a DPDT type, and it is connected in the manner shown in the circuit diagram of Figure 70.

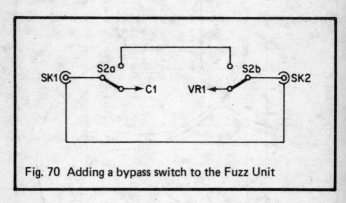

Fig. 70 Adding a bypass switch to the Fuzz Unit

Components for Project 30 – Fuzz Unit (Fig. 68)
  Resistors: all 1/3 watt 5% (10% over 1 M)
R1   100 k (brown, black, yellow, gold)
R2   4.7 k (yellow, violet, red, gold)
R3   4.7 k (yellow, violet, red, gold)
R4   100 k (brown, black, yellow, gold)
R5   10 M (brown, black, blue, silver)
VR1   100 k log. carbon
  Capacitors:
C1   220 nF polyester (red, red, yellow, black, red)
C2   10 μF 25 V electrolytic

148

Semiconductors:

IC1   TLO81CP
D1   1N4148
D2   1N4148

Switch:

S1   SPST miniature toggle type

Sockets:

SK1   6.35 mm standard jack type
SK2   6.35 mm standard jack type

Battery:

B1   PP6 size 9 volt and connector to suit

Miscellaneous:

Verobloc
Control knob
Wire

Please note overleaf is a list of other titles that are available in our range of Radio, Electronics and Computer Books.

These should be available from all good Booksellers, Radio Component Dealers and Mail Order Companies.

However, should you experience difficulty in obtaining any title in your area, then please write directly to the publisher enclosing payment to cover the cost of the book plus adequate postage.

If you would like a complete catalogue of our entire range of Radio, Electronics and Computer Books then please send a Stamped Addressed Envelope to:

BERNARD BABANI (publishing) LTD
THE GRAMPIANS
SHEPHERDS BUSH ROAD
LONDON W6 7NF
ENGLAND